NEWNES INTERNATIONAL MONOGRAPHS ON ELECTRICAL ENGINEERING AND ELECTRONICS

ELECTRONIC SENSING DEVICES

NEWNES INTERNATIONAL MONOGRAPHS ON

ELECTRICAL ENGINEERING AND ELECTRONICS

General Editor

Professor M. G. Say

Ph.D., M.Sc., A.C.G.I., D.I.C., F.I.E.E., M.I.E.R.E., F.R.S.E.

This series of books is the work of specialists who have become deeply experienced in their chosen fields within the general purview of electrical and electronic engineering. It collects and digests material that presents the state of the art in selected developing points in these fields, to give the reader the latest available information on the subject.

Electrical Insulation Measurements

by W. P. Baker, B.Sc. (Eng.)., A.R.T.C.S., F.I.E.E., M.I.E.R.E.

A.E.I. Power Group Research Laboratory

Induction Machines for Special Purposes

by E. R. Laithwaite, D.Sc., Ph.D., F.I.E.E., Mem.I.E.E.E.

Professor of Heavy Electrical Engineering, Imperial College, London

Electronic Sensing Devices

by A. F. Giles, B.Sc., A.R.C.S., M.I.E.R.E., M.Inst.M.C.

Other titles in preparation

ELECTRONIC SENSING DEVICES

by

A. F. Giles

B.Sc., A.R.C.S., M.I.E.R.E., M.Inst.M.C.

With a foreword by

H. A. Thomas

D.Sc., C.Eng., F.I.E.E.

LONDON
GEORGE NEWNES LIMITED
TOWER HOUSE, SOUTHAMPTON STREET
LONDON, W.C.2

First published 1966
Reprinted 1968

MADE AND PRINTED IN GREAT BRITAIN BY
WILLIAM CLOWES AND SONS, LIMITED, LONDON AND BECCLES

CONTENTS

FOREWORD

by H. A. Thomas, D.Sc., C.Eng., F.I.E.E.

The practising engineer engaged in industrial control problems attempts to control the parameters in a process—temperature, pressure, flow, etc.—by introducing sensing devices and pneumatic or electronic controllers. The degree of product consistency obtainable by such 'inferential' control is limited, however, by the cumulative and unpredictable inaccuracies in the sensing devices.

The tendency nowadays is to use, whenever possible, on-stream end-point analytical instruments; determine by experiment the most important parameters in the system that affect the quality of the product; and then utilize the error signals provided by the analytical instruments to control the vital parameters. In industries where satisfactory sensing devices are commercially available, the practising engineer can specify much more sophisticated control equipment and, in consequence, greater profitability can be achieved.

In many industries, however, no adequate control has yet been attained, because either no satisfactory sensing devices have been developed or the control engineer is unaware that sensing devices could be made available to solve his particular problem.

In any controlled system the sensing devices form the first link in a chain of control equipment; they observe what is happening—they take note of product characteristics such as size, weight, temperature, colour, etc.; they act as inspectors noting deviations from the specification. Some of them are substitutes for the human senses—feeling, sight, hearing, taste and smell—while others have 'extra-sensory' characteristics beyond direct human observation, such as moisture measurement, chemical analysis, crack detection and so on.

Although many sensing devices in use today utilize mechanical or pneumatic techniques in their operation, there is a growing awareness of the importance of electronic sensing devices. This is due partly to the steady replacement of pneumatic by electronic process control equipment and partly to the growing incorporation of electronic computers in control systems. In both cases, compatibility of the measuring and control units is of the highest importance.

This book aims at providing assistance to those engaged in developing or applying industrial sensing devices and controllers; whereas there are innumerable books on the fundamentals of electronics, on telecommunication applications and on industrial electronics, there are very few devoted entirely to *Electronic Sensing Devices*.

The author's classification of the manner in which known physical and chemical effects can be utilized is logical and the review in Chapters 7 and 8 of electronic sensing devices of importance in physical measurement and in chemistry should be most helpful.

With an education in pure physics, a graduate apprenticeship in light electrical engineering, and ten years' experience of practical industrial problems in process control and instrumentation, the author is well qualified to present this book to the technologist.

The book undoubtedly fills a gap in technical literature; primarily it is a work of reference, containing between its covers a vast amount of information gleaned from innumerable sources and presented in an easily readable manner.

It should find a place on every control engineer's bookshelf and should stimulate the much-needed development of new devices suitable for utilization in those industries which so far have barely felt the impact of control technology.

PREFACE

We no longer need to apologize for the use of electronic sensing and control devices in industry. A few years ago the majority of industrial processes were manually controlled, with the aid of a few pneumatic and mechanical controllers: electronic devices were considered only as a last resort, being viewed with suspicion by the 'old school' as newfangled contraptions. Now the position is rapidly reversing and soon electronics will be the automatic choice whenever sensing and control problems arise. The development of new devices is proceeding at such a startling pace that, during a two- or three-year period while a new factory or plant is being constructed, techniques chosen at the beginning may become obsolete several times over by the time they are in use. The statement that 'if it works it's obsolete' is often only too true.

It is hoped that this book will be of interest and assistance to those engaged in the development and application of industrial control instruments. It is also hoped that the marshalling of information on sensing methods from such widely differing disciplines as computers and chemistry will spark-off those of an inventive frame of mind to the development of even more new devices. It may also help science and engineering students to understand more clearly the fascinating career in Process Control that has opened up during the last decade.

The main emphasis of the book in Chapters 2–6 is on the use that can be made of the known physical and chemical effects. Chapters 7 and 8 take the opposite point of view in reviewing some of the measurement problems encountered in industry and showing how electronics can assist in their solution.

I would like to express my appreciation to those manufacturers who have supplied information and made suggestions and criticisms of the descriptions of their products in the text. A list of the manufacturers referred to is given at the end of the book. My apologies are due to the many excellent manufacturers, some of whom supplied information on their products, who could not be mentioned for reasons of space. Acknowledgement is also due for permission to reproduce certain items from other publications.

I would like to thank Dr. A. H. Sutton and Mr. M. D. Armitage for their criticism of certain parts of the book, and Mr. G. Gardner who read through the entire manuscript and made many valuable suggestions. Thanks are also due to Dr. H. A. Thomas for his suggestions and guidance in the formative stages of the book. Finally, my grateful acknowledgements are due to Mr. T. F. Saunders of George Newnes Ltd. for his helpful co-operation and advice and to Professor M. G. Say for his many improvements in the arrangement of the text.

A.F.G.

CHAPTER 1

INTRODUCTION

The System Concept

The world in which we live is made up of a multitude of interacting systems, mechanical, electrical, economic, social, etc., which, although differing enormously from each other, have certain features in common. Each aspect of life may be considered as a body from which a controlling intelligence receives information and to which it makes adjustments. The terms sensor and actuator, shown in the basic system of Fig. 1.1, are, perhaps, only applicable to physical systems.

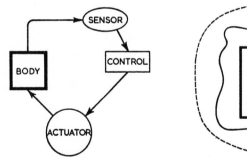

FIG. 1.1. Basic system.

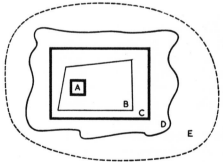

FIG. 1.2. Systems within systems.

Fig. 1.2 illustrates how a number of systems of vastly differing size and importance can exist together. In this diagram

A represents an instrument with its internal feedback control circuits;
B represents an item of process plant on which the instrument is installed;
C represents a factory of which the process plant is an integral part;
D represents the suppliers of raw materials and the consumers of the factory's products together with advertising and marketing activities;

E represents world trade to which the operation of the factory makes a contribution with its imports and exports together with such influences as tariffs, customs duties and other government regulations.

Well-organized systems have a single co-ordinating control although they may have many sensors and actuators. Sometimes badly-organized systems have many controlling influences whose objectives and interests conflict.

The Three Control Questions

There are three kinds of question that a control may ask to obtain information from a sensor. They are: 'is it?', 'how many?' and 'how much?' We must now consider each question in more detail.

1. **Is it?** A microswitch may be used to sense whether a door is open or closed. It then, in effect, answers the question: 'Is it (the door) closed?' The answer is, of course, yes or no. Sensing devices that give this kind of answer are known as on/off devices. Another example of an on/off sensor is a thermostat which closes a contact when the temperature falls below a set value. The question here is: 'Is it (the temperature) below the set point?' 'Yes' is signalled by a closed contact and 'No' by an open contact.

2. **How many?** A photoelectric counter on a conveyer belt may be used to count the number of boxes fed into a store on a given day. This responds to the question 'how many?' with a train of pulses or a coded signal corresponding to the number of boxes. Sometimes a continuous quantity may be sensed in this way to find the number of units involved. For example a telephone timer may record a call in terms of complete minutes irrespective of whether the call is terminated half-way through the last minute.

3. **How much?** Sensors which answer this question are known as analogue sensors. An example is an ammeter which indicates, by the deflection of a pointer, how much current is flowing in a circuit. The deflection of the pointer is thus an analogue of the current.

Information Channels

The information channel from the sensor to the control and from the control to the actuator may take many forms. A few are tabulated here for illustration:

1. **Visual.** A clock or instrument dial presents its information in visual form. Other examples are light signals and visual alarms.

2. **Mechanical.** Transmission of information through rods, levers and wires is still common in railway signalling systems. Another example is a blind man's watch, which tells him the time by touch.

3. **Hydraulic.** In many temperature recorders the temperature is signalled from a sensitive bulb to a bellows or bourdon tube by means of a capillary tube.

4. **Pneumatic.** Pneumatic controllers are very common in industry and usually operate with air signals having values in the range 3–15 lb/in^2.

5. **Electrical.** Most types of information can be signalled by electrical means including, of course, all signals from electronic sensing devices.

6. **Messages.** Under this heading are included memos, letters, instrument charts, production records, etc.

Signals may also differ in their urgency or in how long they are to last. In the human body, one of the most complex systems of all, nerves carry urgent signals, while hormones act as chemical messengers carrying longer-term signals. The duty of sensors, that of getting and supplying information, is one that is done most ably by electronic devices.

Sensors or Transducers?

A transducer converts energy from one form to another whereas a sensor provides an energy signal corresponding to a particular situation. Quite often a sensor is also a transducer, an active device in which a little energy from the quantity being measured is converted to a suitable form for transmission. An example of this is the photovoltaic cell which converts light energy into an electrical potential. Alternatively sensors may be passive devices which require to be excited and then supply information by returning some of the excitation energy. Even these devices use transducing principles to a certain extent because they must absorb some energy from a situation in order to be able to set themselves up to respond correctly to the excitation: thus a photoconductive cell, in which a small quantity of absorbed energy causes a change of resistance, regulates a much larger flow of electrical energy.

A sensing device which monitors a situation but only transmits data on request is known as a transponder. Sometimes many transponders share a common signal channel, coded signals being used to interrogate individual units.

Transducers exist only for a few of all the possible combinations of the different kinds of energy known, although the number is growing as different 'effects' are discovered. Unfortunately many of these effects are not usable for sensing owing to their small magnitude. However, with the progress of science and discovery of new materials, effects only recently regarded as laboratory curiosities have now become useful. Examples are the Hall effect, the Peltier effect and the piezoresistive effect, all of which owe their present usefulness to semiconductor research.

Questions that can be asked by the User

There are a number of questions that arise when considering the suitability of a sensing device for a particular application. The questions are not particular to electronic sensing devices but arise whatever sensor is used.

1. *What effect does the sensing device have on the system (a) initially?, (b) continuously?*

When a thermometer of large thermal mass is placed in a small quantity of water the final temperature reading will not be the same as the original water temperature (unless they were originally at the same temperature). Continuous errors are experienced in the following examples: the flow restriction of a flowmeter, the humidifying effect of a wet- and dry-bulb psychrometer, the heating effect of a resistance thermometer.

2. *What is the response time?*

A thermometer of large thermal mass in air will respond only slowly to changes of air temperature and a considerable time must elapse before the reading will be correct. However, in the meantime the air temperature may have changed and so a correct reading may never be obtained. The response time is usually given as a time-constant T where the reading R_t at time t of an instrument showing an initial reading R_0 and tending to a final reading of R_f is given by

$$R_t = R_f - (R_f - R_0) \exp(-t/T).$$

After a period equal to the time-constant T, an instrument will have moved 0·63 of the way towards the final position. After 4·6T the instrument will have moved 0·99 of the way and after 7T it will have moved 0·999 of the way towards the final position.

The response time does not depend on the sensing device alone, but on the surroundings as well. A thermometer in a stirred tank of liquid will respond quicker than in a perfectly still tank. It will of course have a different response time in another liquid or in air.

3. *What is the repeatability?*

How precisely does the instrument return to the same position each time when measuring the same quantity? An instrument may be incorrectly calibrated and thus inaccurate, yet very repeatable. The photographer's exposure meter and camera may individually be incorrectly calibrated, but the owner knows what settings give the correct results.

4. *What is the linearity?*

Some sensors are claimed to have an output which varies linearly with the quantity being measured. Fig. 1.3 illustrates typical non-linearity caused by second-order effects. Such a response is typical, for example, of poor quality strain-gauge load cells.

5. *Is there any backlash?*

Mechanical backlash is well known as the difference in position caused by slack in gear trains. Where necessary, anti-backlash gears can incorporate springs to take up slack. Alternatively the output shaft can be biased one way. Backlash appears as a difference of reading between a point approached from above and the same point approached from below. Electrical backlash, known as hysteresis, appears in circuits involving the interaction of electric currents and mechanical strain, or magnetic or electrostatic polarization.

6. *What is the sensitivity?*

In other words: what is the smallest change in the input that is registered by the device?

7. *What is the sensitivity to other variables?*

Most sensing devices respond to other than the parameter of interest. For example mercury-in-glass thermometers respond to pressure as well as temperature; photocells usually respond to temperature and other radiation as well as to light.

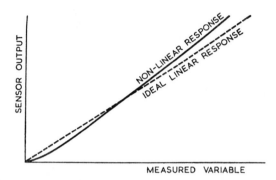

FIG. 1.3. Typical non-linear response.

8. *What is the maximum error?*

The maximum error is likely to be experienced under adverse extremes of all the specified conditions of temperature, pressure, vibration, long-term drift, low supply voltage, etc.

9. *How long will it maintain its accuracy in service?*

Here electronic devices score heavily, as with the absence of moving parts no wear occurs. However, filament lamps gradually change in their output and become less efficient, finally failing completely, and so photo-electric systems employing them may need periodic re-calibration. Some electronic devices themselves change slightly with time but proper choice of components usually eliminates trouble from this source.

10. *Will it stand up to my process liquids?*

Most flowmeters can be supplied in materials suitable for handling difficult and corrosive liquids.

11. *Is the instrument hermetically sealed?*

Unless an instrument is hermetically sealed it is probably best for it to have a hole in the bottom to let water out when intended for use in damp factory atmospheres. Otherwise the 'breathing' that occurs during changes of ambient temperature may slowly pump water into the inside of the instrument case.

12. *For food industry applications. Are there any crevices where bacteria can breed?*

Where this is an acute problem, as in the dairy industry, all parts in contact with the product must be made so that they can be easily stripped down. Additionally, a system of 'cleaning in place' is often used in which detergent and sterilizing fluids are pumped through. The sensing devices must be able to withstand these liquids without damage or subsequent off-flavouring of the product.

Statements of Accuracy

A statement to the effect that an instrument is correct to a certain per cent has no absolute meaning: it is necessary to state to what the percentage relates. If an instrument is quoted as being accurate to, say, ± 1 per cent of *full scale*, then when it reads 20 per cent of full scale the accuracy is only ± 5 per cent of the reading, which is reasonable. If, however, an instrument is quoted as being accurate to ± 1 per cent of the *reading*, then when it indicates 20 per cent of full scale the inferred accuracy is ± 0.2 per cent of full scale, which is unlikely. A safer way is to quote accuracy in terms of units being measured.

Accuracy figures apply to instruments having an analogue or digital readout. With instruments such as check weighers (where a yes/no answer is given to the question: 'is this packet underweight?') the precision of measurement is quoted in terms of a *zone of indecision*. The greater the sensitivity the narrower is the zone of indecision. When an object being weighed is within the zone of indecision the output of the check weigher is indeterminate: it may be yes or no. The width of the zone of indecision corresponds to the width of the $\pm$ (units of accuracy) with analogue or digital instruments. Zones of indecision apply to all forms of trigger and discriminator circuits that have to decide whether a quantity is above a predetermined level or not.

CHAPTER 2

SOLID-STATE SENSORS

The electrical properties of a solid material may be affected by external influences such as heat, light, X-rays and γ-rays, as well as by strains in the material. These effects frequently provide a means for sensing the various conditions. In order to appreciate the various effects it is necessary to consider the structure of atoms and the mechanisms which bring about the conduction of electricity. No more than the briefest of treatments is possible here but it should suffice to put the effects into perspective.

Atomic Structure

Following the pioneer work of Rutherford, Bohr, Pauli and others our knowledge of atomic processes is now firmly based on the principles of wave mechanics. Every atom consists of a positively-charged central core or nucleus surrounded by electrons. The nucleus contains a discrete number of units of positive charge, each unit being equal and of opposite sign to that of an electron. In the case of a normal uncharged atom the positive charge of the nucleus is exactly counterbalanced by the proximity of a corresponding number of electrons. These electrons, although strongly attracted to the nucleus by virtue of their opposite sign, are prevented from falling into the nucleus by the possession of an orbital energy. In the case of the atoms of a gas the orbital energies of the electrons are restricted to a few specific values.

Fig. 2.1 shows the structure of two atoms, neon and sodium, which are almost identical structurally yet vastly different physically. The completely-filled outer level of neon gives rise to its chemical inertness whereas the single outer electron of sodium makes it a very active element. A similar contrast can be seen when the third level is filled, as in argon, and when there is one electron in the fourth level, as in potassium. The territories of electrons, known as orbitals, are represented by undefined shapes in the two dimensions of the paper, although in fact they are three dimensional and overlap each other in space. They are all symmetrical about the nucleus although this cannot be shown on the diagram.

2   7

On receipt of energy, an electron may be raised from the level it is occupying to a higher one. The atom is then said to be excited. This electron is then in an unstable state and soon falls back into its usual place. As it does so it either emits radiation energy (visible light, X-rays, etc.) or its energy appears as heat.

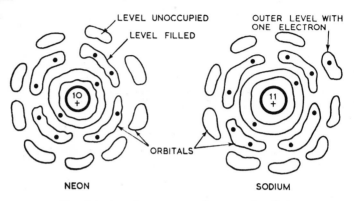

FIG. 2.1. Atomic structures of neon and sodium.

Light energy exists in 'packets' known as quanta and these are of great significance in the interaction of light and matter. The energy E of a quantum is related to the wavelength of light by the formula:

$$E = 1{\cdot}238/\lambda \text{ electron-volts}$$

where λ is wavelength in micrometres. This means, for example, that blue light having a wavelength of 0·4 μm would be associated with an energy of $1{\cdot}238/0{\cdot}4 = 3{\cdot}09$ eV. The significance of this in relation to the emission of light by a gas is that light will be emitted at certain frequencies only, corresponding to specific energy-level differences, so giving rise to the characteristic lines of the spectrum. Similarly, when a gas absorbs energy from light it does so at specific wavelengths causing characteristic dark absorption lines. This principle is used in the infra-red gas analyser described in Chapter 8.

With solid materials it is necessary to consider the bulk effect of many atoms. Broadly speaking, however, the effects described for individual atoms still apply to the *crystalline* structures of metals and semiconductors. The outer atomic electrons, which are responsible for electrical conduction, can be regarded as existing in a cloud throughout the material. The orbital energies are no longer confined to specific values but, due to interaction between atoms, are spread over energy bands. The movement of conduction electrons is not confined to relatively large jumps but may be very small, from one energy level to another in the same energy band. This is illustrated by the fact that the most minute electrical potential differences applied to a metallic conductor are sufficient to cause a current to flow.

The electrons can be considered as having been poured into the energy bands, filling them up to a certain level known as the Fermi level. The potential associated with this level, the Fermi potential, is vitally concerned with electrical conduction, and is less negative than the external potential of a material otherwise referred to as the cavity potential. From the point of view of electrical circuitry the cavity potential is of no significance as it has no effect on currents and voltages in a circuit. The contact potential between different metals, i.e. the difference between their cavity potentials, can only be realized in electrostatic systems where they are occasionally a nuisance. The potential difference between the Fermi potential and the cavity potential is known as the *work function* of a material. This is mentioned in Chapter 4 in connection with photo-emission and is the energy required to remove an electron from the surface of a material.

The practical application of the various electrical conduction effects for sensing will now be examined in turn.

Resistive Strain-gauges

When a conductor is put under mechanical stress it experiences a strain in the direction of the applied stress. As far as conduction of electricity is concerned two effects occur. The first is that the increase in length and decrease in cross-sectional area of the conductor increases its *resistance*. The second depends on the fact that the strain may affect the crystal lattice relationships and alter the *resistivity* of the material; this is known as the piezoresistive effect. In metals the dimensional change is the major factor, whereas in semiconductors the dimensional change is swamped by the resistivity change which may be positive or negative with strain. A measure of the sensitivity of a strain-gauge is the gauge factor, defined as the proportional increase in resistance divided by the proportional increase in length. The following relationships show how the gauge factor is related to the dimensional and piezoresistive effects.

Consider a conductor of length l and cross-sectional area a. The two dimensions of the area at right angles to the direction of stress undergo a negative strain which is related to the longitudinal strain by Poisson's ratio v. Let the longitudinal strain per unit length be (dl/l): then the proportional change in sectional area is

$$(da/a) = [1 - v(dl/l)]^2 - 1 \simeq -2v(dl/l) \qquad (i)$$

ignoring the squared term. The resistance of the conductor is $R = \rho(l/a)$ when unstrained, where ρ is the resistivity. All three of the quantities on the right-hand side are affected by strain; hence, differentiating with respect to l.

$$\frac{dR}{dl} = \rho \frac{d}{dl}\left(\frac{l}{a}\right) + \frac{l}{a}\frac{d\rho}{dl} = \rho \frac{a - l(da/dl)}{a^2} + \frac{l}{a}\frac{d\rho}{dl}.$$

Multiplying by dl and dividing by R gives

$$\frac{dR}{R} = \frac{dl}{l} - \frac{da}{a} + \frac{d\rho}{\rho} = \frac{dl}{l}(1+2\nu) + \frac{d\rho}{\rho} \qquad \text{(ii)}$$

using the relation in eq. (i). Dividing eq. (ii) by (dl/l) gives the gauge factor k_g:

$$k_g = [(dR/R)/(dl/l)] = \underset{\substack{\text{dimensional}\\\text{effect}}}{[1+2\nu]} + \underset{\substack{\text{piezoresistive}\\\text{effect}}}{[(d\rho/\rho)/(dl/l)]} \qquad \text{(iii)}$$

In metals the piezoresistive term is small, and with ν in the range 0·3–0·5, the gauge factor k_g is generally of the order of 2. In semiconductors the piezoresistive term usually predominates.

In general, with n-type silicon and germanium the resistance increases with strain whereas with p-type material the opposite effect is obtained. Unfortunately a (strain)^2 term appears in the analysis of the resistance/strain relationships which often gives rise to a significant non-linearity. There is also often a marked temperature-dependence effect. Gauges are, however, now available in which these effects are minimal due to a careful control of the level of doping of the semiconductor material. When used in transducers, the temperature coefficient of gauge factor can be made equal and opposite to the temperature coefficient of the modulus of elasticity of the deflecting member. It is frequently possible to use matched sets of p-type and n-type gauges to make compound assemblies for load cells, etc., which are substantially free from the errors mentioned.

We have up to now considered strain-gauges in which the resistance change is measured in the direction of the applied stress, the longitudinal effect. The piezoresistive effects of transverse and shear strain are also useful, although sensing devices using these effects are not so common.

Mounting of Strain-gauges

Strain-gauges are used either to measure strain in an existing structure, such as a bridge or aircraft, or as part of a deflecting system such as a load cell. In either case the strain of a main-load-bearing member must be transmitted to the gauge: according to the method chosen for doing this the gauges are classed as bonded, unbonded or integrally-constructed.

Examples of *bonded* strain-gauges are shown in Fig. 2.2. The conductor may be wire, printed circuit or a slice of semiconductor material attached to

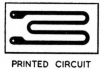
PRINTED CIRCUIT

SLICE OF SEMI-
CONDUCTOR MATERIAL

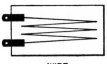
WIRE

FIG. 2.2. Bonded strain-gauges.

a carrier such as paper or plastic film. The strain-gauge is normally bonded to the load-bearing member with epoxy or phenolic resin. The gauge material, its length and bonding agent must be carefully chosen so that slip or yield of the bond does not contribute errors.

Another source of error, arising from the difference of the thermal expansion of the gauge and the load-bearing structure, can be overcome by selecting gauges with a coefficient of expansion similar to that of the main structure, or by mounting one or more gauges on a piece of similar (but unstressed) material at the same temperature as the load-bearing member. The output from these can then be used to correct the main strain-gauges. Another method employs a platinum resistance-thermometer attached to the same insulating mount as the strain-gauge. The platinum resistance is connected in an appropriate arm of the bridge circuit and adjusted to correct operation by variation of series and parallel resistors.

A diagram of a tension load-cell incorporating four strain-gauges is shown in Fig. 2.3. Two of the gauges are set along the direction of tension and two

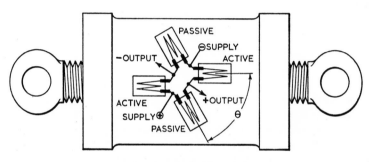

FIG. 2.3. Tension load-cell.

are at an angle θ to the tension, a position of zero strain when $\tan \theta = 1/\nu$, where ν is Poisson's ratio for the base material. The four gauges enable a bridge circuit to be used for measuring and the two neutral gauges compensate for temperature effects. Compressive load-cells using pillars or rings are also common.

Errors due to imperfections of the bonding agent or carrier material are eliminated if the strain-gauge consists of wire wound directly on a former which alters its dimension with strain. This principle is being used extensively for accelerometers and pressure gauges. An example of the latter is shown in Fig. 7.12. Movement of the diaphragm is transmitted to a spring structure on which are mounted four insulating posts. Two strain-gauge windings are mounted on the posts on each side of the spring. Some initial tension is present in the wires so that they do not become slack when their tension is decreased. Very rugged devices, capable of meeting missile and space requirements, are standard practice with this method.

Strain-gauge mounting problems disappear completely in the integrally-formed semiconductor gauge. The main strain member is a slab of silicon and the strain-sensitive elements are formed by diffusing an impurity directly into the slab. The slab may be of high purity or have impurities of a type opposite to those of the strain-gauge, so that the p–n junction thus formed can isolate one from the other.

Strain-gauge Circuits

Where a single gauge gives satisfactory linearity and temperature-independence, it is best operated from a constant-current source such as that shown in Fig. 2.4. A more usual arrangement is the Wheatstone bridge

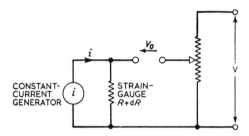

Fig. 2.4. Single gauge constant-current circuit.

circuit using two or four strain-gauges. These may comprise two active and two passive gauges as in Fig. 2.5 (*a*), one positive and one negative acting gauge with two resistors as in (*b*) or four active gauges as in (*c*). Devices using one or other of these arrangements are usually specified to be operated from a stabilized-voltage supply. The output is in the form of a voltage generator in series with a source resistance which varies with the strain. The presence of a strain-dependent term in the source resistance means that the output circuit must be of high impedance to avoid non-linearity from this source. The main disadvantage of a bridge circuit is the absence of a common terminal between the power supply and detector. The need to provide a separate power supply to energize the bridge can, however, be eliminated by using a signal amplifier

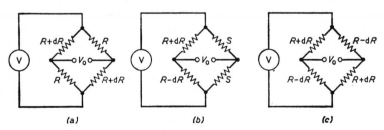

Fig. 2.5. Constant-voltage strain-gauge bridge circuits.

with differential input. In the past a.c. excitation of strain-gauge bridges has been popular but with the greatly improved d.c. amplifiers now available there is little reason to use a.c.

With the exception of certain devices specially compensated for working with a constant voltage supply there is an advantage in working a bridge of four active arms with a constant-current supply as in Fig. 2.6. The output of the bridge to the measuring circuit appears as a voltage generator $i.dR$ in series with a resistance R. This can be measured with a virtually short-circuit input amplifier provided R remains constant.

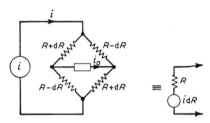

FIG. 2.6. Constant-current bridge circuit.

There is sometimes a case for using a bridge supply intermediate between constant voltage and constant current, i.e., a supply with a specified source impedance. This is of advantage when using gauges which have a small negative temperature-coefficient of gauge factor and a positive temperature-coefficient of resistance. As the temperature increases and output tends to fall, the resistance increases and thus the voltage across the bridge can be made to increase by exactly the amount required to compensate.

Resistance Thermometry

The electrical resistivity of most materials is a function of temperature. In the case of pure metals an increase in temperature leads to an increase in resistivity, attributable to the fact that conduction electrons are impeded in their flow through a metal by thermal agitation. In some alloys such as Constantan, Eureka and Manganin, chosen for the manufacture of resistors, there is only a very small temperature coefficient of resistance. In semi-conductors, although the process of impeding electron movement still operates as in metals, it is often swamped by the greater numbers of electrons made available for conduction by the thermal energy. Consequently most (but not all) semiconductors have a negative temperature coefficient of resistance. Thermistors are negative-temperature-coefficient resistors manu-factured from metal oxide. The field of precision temperature measurement has long been led by pure-metal resistance thermometers, but there is little doubt that they will give way to semiconductor devices of much greater sensitivity. The early thermistors were subject to drift, but this is being remedied as new devices are developed. In particular, silicon positive-temperature-coefficient devices now available offer both high output and high stability.

Metal Resistance Thermometers

The principal metals used are platinum and nickel. The resistance/temperature relation for platinum is given by the formulae:

Above 0°C: $\quad R_\theta = R_0[1 + \alpha\theta + \beta\theta^2]$

Below 0°C: $\quad R_\theta = R_0[1 + \alpha\theta + \beta\theta^2 + \gamma(\theta - 100)\theta^3]$

where $\alpha = +3.958 \times 10^{-3}$, $\beta = -0.583 \times 10^{-6}$ and $\gamma = -3.14 \times 10^{-12}$.

For industrial use resistance thermometers are sealed into metal pockets with terminations to suit the environment. The pocket adds considerable thermal mass to the thermometer and although this is of little consequence when measuring the temperature of liquids, it slows the response when measuring still air temperatures. Another point to watch when measuring air temperatures is the self-heating effect of the resistance thermometer: in unfavourable circumstances this error can be as much as 4°C. The self-heating effect is negligible when measuring liquids because of the much higher conductivity and thermal mass of the surrounding material.

Resistance thermometers are specified by the resistance material and either the resistance at a particular temperature, or the 'fundamental interval' (abbreviated f.i.) which is the change in resistance from 0°C to 100°C. One particular thermometer in common use is platinum 50 f.i. This has a resistance of 130 Ω at 0°C and 180 Ω at 100°C. The resistor may be made as small as the skill of the manufacturer allows by using very thin wire. Thermometers fulfilling the platinum 50 f.i. specification have been wound small enough to fit into the top of a hypodermic needle for medical purposes.

Semiconductor Temperature Sensors

The high sensitivity of thermistors has facilitated the development of small portable electrical thermometers in which temperature is indicated on a meter without the need for amplification. The small thermal mass is very useful in medical applications eliminating the delay of $\frac{1}{2}$ to 1 min required for mercury-in-glass clinical thermometers to attain their proper reading. Where it is required to be able to use a number of thermistor probes with one temperature meter it is necessary to include a coefficient-correction circuit into the plug of each thermistor lead, as it is not yet possible to manufacture thermistors to precise values of resistance as is done with platinum and nickel resistance thermometers.

An important use of thermistors is for inclusion in circuits to correct for other components that have a positive temperature-coefficient. In particular, precision transistor measuring circuits and electrolyte measuring circuits often incorporate thermistors. The variation of the base/emitter voltage of a transistor with temperature (an embarrassment to the designer of d.c. amplifiers) can also be used as a convenient way of measuring temperature. This effect is used in the thermostat circuit of Fig. 2.7. Starting from cold, the high base/emitter voltage prevents the transistor from passing current and a 'normally-operated' contact on the relay energizes the heater, thus warming up the environment. When the base/emitter voltage has fallen, due to the temperature rise, below the value set by the potentiometer, the relay is operated and the heating cut off.

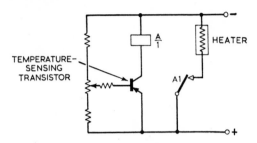

FIG. 2.7. Transistor as temperature sensor.

Self-balancing Bridges

Self-balancing resistance bridges for the indication and recording of temperatures are in common use in a number of industries. The bridges are superficially similar to self-balancing potentiometers described later in this chapter. There are two configurations, strip chart and circular chart. A diagram of the basic mechanical and circuit essentials of a strip-chart recorder is shown in Fig. 2.8. Variations on this theme are supplied by a number of reputable instrument manufacturers and a high standard of reliability is achieved.

Strip-chart recorders may be either single-point or multipoint. Single-point recorders may use ordinary paper charts with ink or ball-point pens. Another variation, more common with smaller instruments, is the use of a special heat-, pressure- or voltage-sensitive paper with a suitable stylus. Multi-point recorders may print numbers or symbols corresponding to the various points scanned and the printing may be in a single colour or multicoloured. A multiway switch is used to select thermometers for print-out on multipoint instruments.

By supplying the bridge with a.c. the error signal is also a.c., so simplifying amplification and drive of the balancing motor. The effect of lead resistance is eliminated by having three equal wires connected as shown. The lead resistance R_{L1} has no effect on balance because it is in series with the supply; the other two, R_{L2} and R_{L3}, are in opposite arms of the bridge and so do not upset balance. The balanced bridge circuit gives good rejection of common-

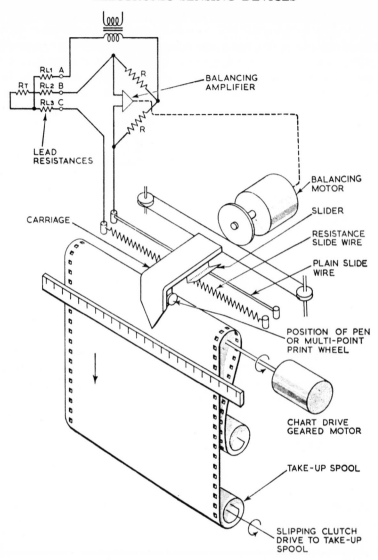

FIG. 2.8. Strip chart self-balancing bridge.

mode interference (i.e., pick-up of spurious signals on the wires leading to terminals B and C).

There are a number of variables which must be specified to the manufacturer on ordering, including:

1. Type of resistance thermometer.

2. Scale range.
3. Single-point or multipoint.
4. Chart speed (may be variable on the instrument).
5. Printing rate (on multipoint instruments).
6. Balance motor speed.
7. Mains supply voltage and frequency.

Thermal-conductivity Detectors

When a resistance thermometer is heated by an electric current its temperature, and thus its resistance, depends on the thermal properties of the medium surrounding it. This effect has been used in a number of devices which give a measure of various properties by inference from thermal effects.

Thermal Flowmeter

The simplest form is the hot-wire anemometer, which utilizes the cooling effect of a moving current of air on a heated wire to cause a change of resistance. The method is well suited to the measurment of low air velocities of the order of 0·1 to 10 m/s. Variations in air temperature have little effect if the wire temperature is appreciably higher than that of the ambient air.

A device for measuring low air-flow rates uses two heated resistance thermometers located either inside a tube or wound round the outside. With no flow the temperature distribution is symmetrical about the centre of the heaters. When gas flows it tends to cool the first heater, the gas itself becoming warm in the process. As the gas is warm it cools the second heater less than the first and thus an unbalanced condition is set up, the degree of which is a measure of the product of flow rate and specific heat. Flow rates as low as 1 cm³/h can be measured if special precautions are taken, otherwise a normal working minimum is about 100 cm³/h.

A particular application of the thermal flowmeter is for measuring the 'magnetic wind' generated in some forms of paramagnetic oxygen analyser, described in Chapter 8.

Katharometer

This is a device for detecting the presence of gases by their differing thermal conductivity compared to a reference gas. It consists essentially of a metal block with a passage for gas flow and a cavity into which a heated resistance thermometer is mounted. Fig. 2.9 shows a typical cell arrangement from a comprehensive range manufactured by Loenco, Inc. The resistance thermometer is shielded from the main gas flow to reduce mass-flow sensitivity. Too much screening causes an unduly long time-constant, and different types of shield are available so that an acceptable compromise may be found. The metal block is usually maintained at constant temperature.

The most sensitive form of katharometer used for gas chromatography consists of a metal block with two gas passages, one for the sample gas and

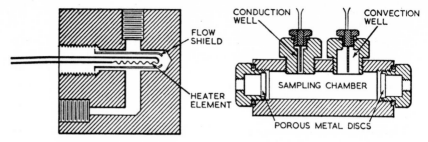

FIG. 2.9. Thermal conductivity cell.
(*Loenco, Inc.*)

FIG. 2.10. Thermatron type M cell.
(*Mine Safety Appliances Company*)

one for the reference gas. Each passage contains two cavities each with a heated resistance thermometer. These are then connected in the form of a Wheatstone bridge or in a constant-current circuit similar to that described for strain gauges. The thermal conductivities of a number of common gases are shown in Table 2.1. Common carrier gases are hydrogen and argon, which differ widely in thermal conductivity. When hydrogen is used as the carrier, then the arrival of hydrocarbon gases at the detector having conductivities in the range 20–80 causes the resistance thermometer to have peaks of higher temperature due to their decreased thermal conductivity.

Table 2.1. Thermal Conductivities of Gases

Gas	Thermal conductivity at 20°C microcal/cm s °C
Hydrogen	420
Helium	350
Methane	76
Oxygen	60
Air	60
Nitrogen	60
Carbon monoxide	57
Argon	41
Carbon dioxide	37
Ethyl alcohol	35

The normal katharometer used with mixtures of three or more gases is unable to distinguish between variations in thermal conductivity due to changing concentration of the gas to be measured, and that due to changes in concentration of the other gases present. In the Thermatron type M cell (Mine Safety Appliances Co.), shown in cross section in Fig. 2.10, selectivity towards one gas is achieved by using different-sized wells. The heated resistance elements mounted in them are differently affected by conduction and convection according to the size of the well and, since convection depends upon other physical properties, it is possible to adjust the circuit to obtain maximum response for the component of interest while variations due to the other components are cancelled out. Porous metal discs at the inlet and outlet of the chamber reduce turbulence and act as heat exchangers and flashback arrestors.

Pirani Gauge

The Pirani gauge, which depends on the variation of thermal conductivity of a gas with pressure, is a useful method of measuring vacuum pressures ranging from 10^{-3} torr to 100 torr. The usual configuration is a negative-temperature-coefficient resistor mounted in a gauge head in contact with the gas, another similar resistor being in contact with the wall of the gauge head. The two resistors are arranged in a Wheatstone bridge circuit with suitable potentials so that a heating effect occurs in the sensing resistors. The actual bridge potential is adjusted, either manually or by a control amplifier, to maintain a constant temperature difference between the two sensing resistors. This temperature difference is usually chosen to be in the range 50–100°C. The bridge input voltage necessary to maintain this condition is thus a measure of the heating current and in turn a measure of the thermal conductivity and vacuum pressure. Variations of the Pirani gauge are also in common use where resistors are used for heating as before but the temperatures are measured by thermocouples.

Thermocouples

There can be few measurements so easy to apply and yet so little understood as thermoelectrical temperature measurements. The main point to establish is that thermoelectric potentials are generated in conductors as a result of thermal gradients, and that no potentials are developed across metal junctions. The misconception about potentials across junctions arises from the need to use two metals in order to get an observable effect. The original *Seebeck effect* gives no clue as to where the observed potential difference arises. In terms of the atomic structure discussed at the beginning of this chapter, when two dissimilar metals are put in contact their Fermi potentials rapidly become equal although there may be a difference of cavity potentials. It is the Fermi potentials that govern the flow of electric current in a circuit: the cavity potentials have no circuit effect. The thermoelectric effects in materials arise from the interaction of the flow of heat, the flow of electric charge and the Fermi potentials. The majority of thermoelectric effects, particularly at low temperatures, still await satisfactory explanation.

Fig. 2.11 shows the essential features of a Seebeck thermocouple system in which the conductors are of materials M_1 and M_2 with junctions at absolute temperatures T_1 and T_2. One conductor is discontinuous, and a potential difference measuring device is connected across its ends. If we assume for convenience that the measuring instrument is at temperature T_1, then the observed potential is the difference in the p.d's across M_1 and M_2 subjected to the same temperature gradient. The majority of published thermocouple tables quote figures for pairs of materials made up into couples in this way. A more fundamental quantity is the Seebeck coefficient S, otherwise known as the absolute thermoelectric power of a material, quoted in microvolts per deg C. This is the thermoelectric potential gradient divided by the temperature gradient for a material at a given temperature. It might be wondered how, if two metals are always necessary to observe an effect, it is ever possible to measure the quantity S for a material on its own. Fortunately, two methods are known; the simpler uses the fact that superconducting metals have no thermoelectric effects. Now as metals have different transition temperatures, it is possible to make up a couple with one metal superconducting, and thus establish the Seebeck coefficient for the other. Lead is often used for this purpose as its transition temperature is about $7°K$, although the compound Nb_3Sn is superconducting up to about $18°K$.

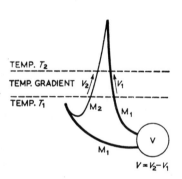

FIG. 2.11. Seebeck effect.   FIG. 2.12. Seebeck coefficient for
                                     copper and constantan.

Although not directly connected with sensing we must briefly consider the other two thermoelectric effects. The *Peltier* effect is the reversible heating or cooling of a junction between two metals that occurs when a current is passed. Although the Peltier heat appears at a junction it is not actually generated there but is swept to the region of the junction by the movement of electrons. The *Thomson* effect occurs when a current flows in a conductor which has a temperature gradient existing in it. According to whether S is positive or negative so the current will tend either to increase or decrease the temperature gradient.

There are two practical laws which are obvious from the 'gradient' approach but should be stated for completeness.

(i) *The law of intermediate metals.* The two metals forming a thermocouple may be joined by a third metal without altering the effect, provided that all the parts are at the same temperature.

(ii) *The law of intermediate temperatures.* Provided that a conductor is of one material it makes no difference what the temperatures are along its length if the ends are at the same temperature.

The validity of the law of intermediate temperatures was challenged by Benedicks, who claimed that uneven temperature gradients in a conductor gave rise to another form of thermoelectric potential. It is now believed that such effects as have been observed arise from inhomogeneity in the conductor, and as such are really only a manifestation of the normal Seebeck effect.

Data on the Seebeck coefficient of materials in common use is neither plentiful nor consistent. Fig. 2.12 shows approximate curves for copper and constantan. The area between the curves at any two temperatures is the potential obtained from a thermocouple circuit. The diagram shows the output with the hot and cold junctions at 100°C and 0°C respectively.

Thermocouple Systems

Of all the combinations of different metals that produce a thermoelectric effect, relatively few are in common use. The main requirement for a pair of metals is that, over the temperature range of interest, the output voltage shall increase approximately linearly with temperature. Copper and iron, for example, are not used together because although the output increases with iron positive at the hot junction up to about 250°C, thereafter it decreases until, beyond 500°C, copper becomes positive. Similar effects occur with many other couples.

There are two main classes of thermocouples, base metal and rare metal. The rare-metal thermocouples, based on platinum and its alloys, have the advantage of high precision at high temperatures although the output in terms of microvolts per degree is much less than for the base-metal couples.

Table 2.2. Properties of Common Thermocouples

Couple	Copper/ Constantan	Iron/ Constantan	Chromel/ Alumel	Platinum/ Platinum- Rhodium*
Sensitivity, μV/°C at 0°C	42	53	41	6·4
Useful range, °C	−200 to +350	−200 to +900	−200 to +1100	0 to +1400

* 10 per cent rhodium

Table 2.2 compares the properties of a few of the more commonly used thermocouples.

For industrial use in process plant, thermocouples are mounted in a metal sheath which may itself be mounted in a pocket immersed in the process liquid. In this application there is little to choose between thermocouples and resistance thermometers. One particular advantage of the thermocouple in certain other applications is its small thermal mass and consequential response to rapid changes of temperature.

When an expensive precision thermocouple material is being used and it is required to make measurements some distance from the measuring instrument it is often possible to use a cheaper wire for interconnection. This 'compensating cable' is chosen to have a sensitivity approximately equal to that of the precision material in use. For example, a specially matched copper/copper–nickel wire pair can be used to connect a platinum/platinum–rhodium couple. As compensating cable cannot be expected to have exactly the same characteristics as the main couple some limitations in its use should be observed. For example, the joints at both ends should be in an ambient temperature that changes only slightly compared with the temperature being measured, otherwise the error voltage due to mismatch of characteristics will be too great. This means that the use of compensating cable is confined to the measurement of hot objects where the junction between the precision thermocouple and compensating cable is outside the hot zone, and is not suitable for connecting cold-store or refrigerator thermocouples where variations in ambient temperature are certain to exceed the variations in the temperature being measured. For these applications, where base-metal thermocouples are almost invariably used, the same type and grade of thermocouple material should be used throughout.

Self-balancing Potentiometers

Although sensitive galvanometer indicators can be used to display the higher ranges of temperature, electronic self-balancing potentiometers have now become well established for precision work. These instruments are similar to the self-balancing bridges used for resistance thermometers described earlier. Fig. 2.13 shows the essential features. The potentiometer error signal is amplified, usually in an amplifier with a mechanical chopper, and the output used to drive the carriage to balance. The reference junction is not held at a constant temperature but is allowed to assume the ambient temperature of the inside of the instrument case. A resistance thermometer integral with the reference thermocouple is incorporated into the potentiometer circuit to compensate for variations of ambient temperature. It is usual with multipoint instruments to use switch wipers and contacts made of the thermocouple materials (or their equivalent) so that, for example, a constantan wire is connected via a constantan conduction path to the reference junction. The only exceptions are the solder tags or terminals used for connection.

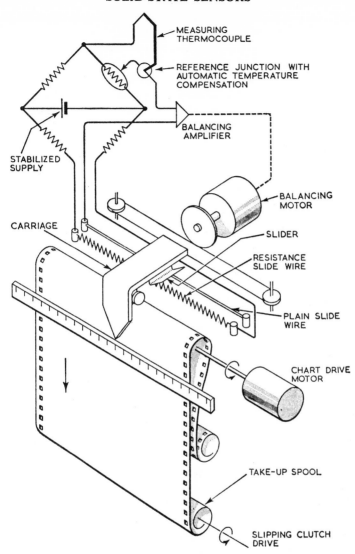

FIG. 2.13. Strip chart self-balancing potentiometer.

Measurements involving Differential Temperatures

Differential temperatures can readily be measured with thermocouple systems by putting the two junctions at the temperatures whose difference is to be measured. No problem arises with the connecting leads as these can both be made of the same material. There are several instruments that use a number of differential thermocouples in series, an arrangement known as a

3

thermopile. Fig. 2.14 shows a sectional view of the Ardonox radiation pyrometer in which thermal radiation is focused on to a thermopile and compensation for variations of ambient temperature is made with a resistance thermometer. An amplifier is incorporated to increase the signal level for display. This instrument is not limited to high-temperature applications: it will measure temperatures from +600°C down to −40°C. When measuring temperatures below ambient there is a net heat flow from the thermopile to the object whose temperature is being measured. Another similar instrument, the Ardometer, using a quartz lens instead of a concave mirror, is suitable for measuring temperatures in the range 400–2000°C.

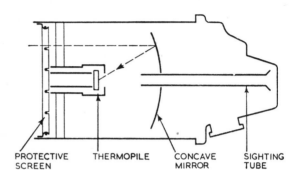

PROTECTIVE   THERMOPILE   CONCAVE   SIGHTING
SCREEN   MIRROR   TUBE

Fig. 2.14. Ardonox radiation pyrometer. (*Siemens & Halske*)

An ingenious thermopile developed by the T.N.O. and T.H. in Delft, enables heat flows through thin layers to be measured. It consists of a piece of material of known thermal conductivity on which is wound a single layer of fine constantan wire. Half of the winding is then copper plated as shown in Fig. 2.15. As the copper is a much better conductor than constantan, the copper plated wire has an effect equivalent to solid copper wire. Although the temperature drop due to heat flow over the thin layer is very small the effect is observable owing to the large number of thermocouples in series.

Another device using a series of thermocouples is the neutron thermopile, in which alternate junctions are coated with boron. This material gets warm under the action of the neutrons and the resulting voltage output is a measure of the neutron flux density. The device is simple, the main disadvantage being the slow response time, of the order of seconds.

Photoconductivity

In metals, as mentioned earlier in this chapter, there are always electrons available for carrying an electric current through the material, and associated with a typical energy level known as the Fermi level. In insulators there is a considerable gap between the highest filled energy band and any available conduction band. As it is not possible for electrons to have energy in this range it is called a 'forbidden zone'. No electrons are available for conduction under normal conditions; but extreme external forces are able to pull electrons across the forbidden zone and the insulator is then said to have broken down.

Semiconductors, which form a third category of materials intermediate between conductors and insulators, are characterized by a narrow gap between the filled band (the valency band) and the conduction band. Their ability to conduct electricity depends entirely on electrons being excited into the conduction band by thermal energy or some other form of energy. Cadmium-sulphide and lead-sulphide photoconductive cells operate on this principle. They consist of an assembly of two metal electrodes on either side of a piece of semiconductor material. The action of incident light excites electrons into the conduction band but is unable to keep them there. As an electron is only 'conductive' while it is in the conduction band, the sensitivity of the device depends on the time that elapses before the electron falls back.

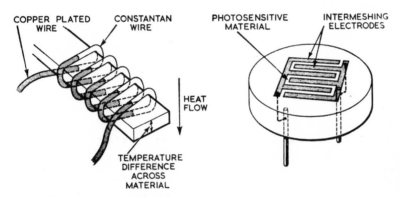

FIG. 2.15. Thermopile heat flowmeter.   FIG. 2.16. Photoconductive cell.

The addition of small quantities of certain impurities increases the time for which electrons remain excited. These impurities, known as traps, offer temporary homes for the excited electrons, thus increasing the time they are available for conduction. (The action of the impurities is quite different from the trivalent or pentavalent doping materials added to silicon and germanium, discussed in the next section.) Photoconductive cells operate as pure resistors with no rectifying action. The current path is made very wide to lower the cell resistance without decreasing the active area by an intermeshing arrangement of the electrodes illustrated in Fig. 2.16. Sensitivity is greatest towards the infra-red end of the spectrum, particularly with lead sulphide. The resistance of a typical cell changes from about 10 MΩ in the dark to 1 kΩ when brightly illuminated.

Photo-diodes and Photo-transistors

Germanium and silicon are well known as the active elements used for making transistors. Both are tetravalent elements which form crystal structures in which each valency electron is shared between two atoms. The effect of this, as shown in Fig. 2.17, is that each atom has the extremely stable arrangement of a completely-equipped valency bond. In itself, this is not a criterion for semiconduction as there are other tetravalent elements that form this kind of structure. The real criterion, as mentioned in the last section, is that there is a narrow forbidden zone between the filled valency band and the conduction band.

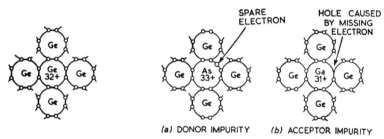

FIG. 2.17. Valence
bonds in pure
germanium.

(a) DONOR IMPURITY   (b) ACCEPTOR IMPURITY

FIG. 2.18. The effect of added impurities.

An interesting and useful change in the situation takes place when small quantities of a trivalent or pentavalent element are added. As can be seen in Fig. 2.18, the pentavalent element arsenic fits readily into the lattice, and as each atom donates a spare electron, the element is referred to as a 'donor' additive. The few donated electrons are free to move about the crystal but do not give rise to increased negative charge because of the extra positive charges in the nuclei of the donor atoms. Similarly the trivalent gallium contributes vacancies in the valency bond into which electrons may move, giving an 'acceptor' impurity. Thus we are able to produce semiconductors with an excess of electrons (n-type) or an excess of vacancies or holes (p-type). In n-type material electrons are referred to as majority carriers and the few holes present due to thermal or other excitation are referred to as minority carriers. In p-type material, holes are the majority carriers and electrons are minority carriers. Although holes behave as positive charges that move around, the effect is really a movement of electrons at valency level.

An extremely small amount of doping material is required to produce an effect on the conductivity. Consider pure germanium, which has 1.77×10^{23} molecules per cm³: each molecule has potentially four conduction electrons but only a small proportion will be in the conduction band at any given instant due to thermal excitation. If the energy gap between the valency and conduction bands is 0·7 V and the thermal excitation is 0·025 V, typical of a temperature of 25°C, the proportion k of electrons in the conduction band is given by $k = \exp(-0.7/0.025)$. This gives a figure of 1.2×10^{11} conduction electrons per cm³. If arsenic is added in the proportion of 1 part in 3×10^7 this produces $(1.77 \times 10^{23})/(3 \times 10^7) = 5.9 \times 10^{15}$ electrons/cm³. Thus the conductivity is increased by $(5.9 \times 10^{15})/(1.2 \times 10^{11})$, or 5.4×10^4 times the value for pure germanium.

The Fermi level of a semiconductor lies between the valence band and conduction band as electrons spend part of their time in each region. The addition of a doping material shifts the Fermi potential as shown in Fig. 2.19.

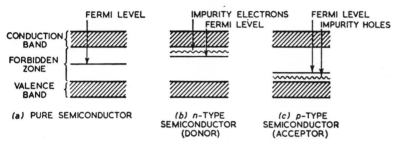

FIG. 2.19. The effect of impurities on Fermi level.

When the two types of material are formed so that they are in contact, a few electrons of the n-type material diffuse across the junction in an attempt to equalize the population of electrons, as the p-type material has very few conduction electrons. At the same time the holes of the p-type material diffuse across to equalize the distribution of holes, Fig. 2.20. The passage of

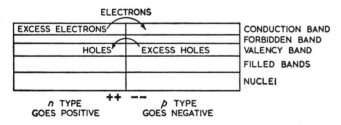

FIG. 2.20. Movement of electrons and holes across a p–n junction.

charge carriers across the junction creates an unbalance of charge between one side of the junction and the other. The consequent distribution of charges and potential appear as in Fig. 2.21. This potential difference does not normally appear across the output terminals as there is an equal and opposite effect at the metal end contacts. In terms of Fermi levels at the junction, the

Fermi level of the *n*-type must rise and that of the *p*-type must decrease until they are equal. The potential barrier then appears as a difference of contact potential.

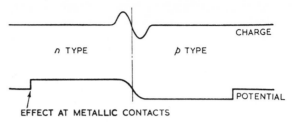

Fig. 2.21. Variation of charge and potential across a *p–n* junction.

When p.d's are applied to the diode terminals they either decrease or increase the height of the potential barrier according to polarity. When the barrier is reduced by the applied potential, majority carriers flow unhindered across the junction and the diode is said to be forward biased. When a reverse bias is applied only the minority carriers are able to cross the junction. This is the most useful condition for sensing. Either light, α-, β- or X-rays may be used as the source of energy to produce the minority carriers and thus the device becomes a detector for these forms of energy.

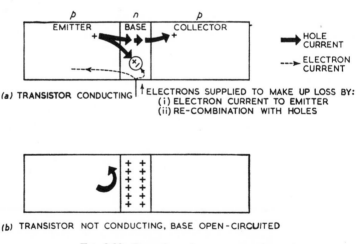

Fig. 2.22. Operation of a *p–n–p* transistor.

Practical photodiodes are constructed in such a way that the light to be sensed can reach the junction area. Phototransistors are an extension of the diode effect to include the amplification of a transistor. Fig. 2.22 illustrate the mechanism of a *p–n–p* transistor; an *n–p–n* type would be the same excep that all the polarities would be reversed. Fig. 2.22(a) shows a normal transistor passing a current. The emitter/base junction is forward-biased and the base/collector junction is reverse biased. The base is less heavily doped than the emitter so the main current from emitter to base consists of holes from the emitter. A small electron current does however flow from the base to the emitter. As the base is very thin, most of the holes reach the collector junction without recombining in the base area. They are then swept away into the collector. For this situation to continue it is necessary for the base circuit to supply electrons for the two purposes shown, namely the small electron current to the emitter and to replace electrons that recombine with holes in the base. Only a small base current is required for the purpose, so that in this way a small current controls a large one and a current amplification is obtained. When the base current is withheld, as in Fig. 2.22(b), the base becomes positively charged. The positive charge repels holes in the emitter and the collector current is reduced to that of minority carriers.

The electrons required by the base can also be supplied from hole-electron pairs produced by light or thermal energy. The way phototransistors operate is illustrated in Fig. 2.23. The holes produced merely add to the existing hole

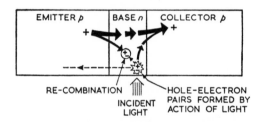

FIG. 2.23. Operation of a *p–n–p* photo-transistor.

current. Phototransistors are often operated with an open-circuited base, however; if the transistor is required to pass no current until a predetermined light level is reached then a small reverse bias may be applied to the base. Alternatively for some control applications the transistor is arranged to be 'turned on' either by the action of light or by forward-biasing the base.

Solid-state Radiation Detectors

Solid-state radiation detectors are becoming increasingly important as detectors of α and β particles, γ-rays and X-rays. The principle of operation is the same as that of photodiodes with light, except that while light energy does not penetrate the material to any great extent the other radiation and particles certainly do. At a *p–n* junction the majority carriers are forced back from the junction area so forming a depletion layer, the depth of which may be varied by applying a bias voltage. It is this depletion volume that is sensitive to the radiation and particles. All α particles entering the depletion volume come to rest in a few microns, producing hole-electron pairs on their way. The β particles, requiring a few millimetres to come to rest, almost certainly pass right through the depletion volume and relatively less hole-electron pairs are produced. The same situation exists with γ-rays and X-rays.

Although p–n junctions of conventional design operate as radiation detectors there is much to be said for a simpler modification employing a slab of semiconductor material with metal contacts on each side. One contact consists of a very thin layer of gold, which acts as a transparent window to the radiation. The depletion volume is formed just behind the gold window.

The Photovoltaic Effect

In the description of the photo-diode it was stated that there is no change of Fermi potential either at the p–n junction or at the end contacts so a potential difference does not appear at the terminals. This is no longer true when the junction is illuminated, as the inflowing light energy upsets the Fermi potential equilibrium and a potential difference then appears. A current may be taken from the device which then acts as a converter from light to electrical energy. Devices made from silicon specially for this application, known as solar cells, achieve an energy conversion efficiency of about 10 per cent.

Another well-established photovoltaic device is the selenium cell, a layer of selenium deposited on a metal plate with a transparent gold film deposited on the selenium. Contact is made with the metal base and the transparent gold film. Barrier potentials are set up between each electrode and the selenium, which in the dark cancel out and no output voltage is produced. When light passes through the gold film into the upper barrier layer, hole-electron pairs are produced. The holes and electrons are drawn in opposite directions across the potential barrier and the gold film attains a negative potential. Sufficient output can be obtained from cells of this type to operate a moving-coil meter; this is the basis of photo-electric exposure meters. Selenium is particularly suitable as its spectral response is approximately the same as that of the human eye. An even better match can be obtained if filters are used. The output is approximately linear with light intensity if a resistance of about 100 Ω is connected across the terminals as, for example, when using a normal milliammeter. With a high-impedance measuring device of impedance greater than about 2 kΩ, then the output is logarithmic with light intensity.

The Piezoelectric Effect

The piezoelectric effect is a reversible relation between the mechanical strain and the charge which appears across the faces of certain crystals, notably quartz, Rochelle salt and ammonium dihydrogen phosphate. As with any uncharged solid, the total positive charge in a crystal cancels the total negative charge. However, when the crystal is strained, some of the positive charges are moved slightly in one direction and some of the negative charges in the opposite direction, and a net charge difference appears on certain of the crystal faces. For the effect to occur there must be an asymmetry of atoms in the direction of the applied stress. A quartz crystal consists of a hexagonal pillar, Fig. 2.24. Its crystallographic axes are defined as follows: the z-axis

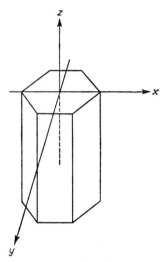

FIG. 2.24. Quartz crystal axes.

(optical axis) is the long axis parallel to all the sides; the x-axis is chosen as one of the lines joining opposite corners and is at right angles to the z-axis; the y-axis is a line joining opposite faces and is at right angles to the x and z axes. Planes are defined by the axis to which they are normal. Thus no piezo-electrical effects are observed in the z plane of quartz but they are observed in the x and y planes. Slices of crystal are known as x-cut or y-cut if they are in the x plane or y plane respectively. Fig. 2.25 represents a cube of quartz and shows that the application of a mechanical force along the x-axis generates a charge difference on faces x_1 and x_2 proportional to the applied stress. The faces y_1 and y_2 move apart as a result of the x compression. A similar effect is obtained if a tension is applied along the y-axis. If a potential is applied to

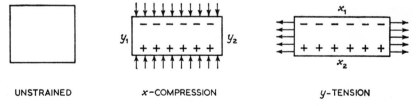

UNSTRAINED x-COMPRESSION y-TENSION

FIG. 2.25. Effect of compression and tension in quartz.

the x-faces the mechanical movements are in the same direction as would have generated the potential.

The faces of quartz and other similar crystals are, of course, planes related to the crystal structure. This has been found a disadvantage in some applications where a focusing effect is required. Fortunately the development of ferroelectric ceramics, which can be of any shape, has satisfied such a requirement. All solid dielectrics exhibit a phenomenon known as the electrostrictive effect, whereby a potential appears across the material proportional to the square of the strain. The effect is usually very small and as the strain is squared the output does not change sign with reversal of strain. It has been found that in certain ceramics the electrostrictive effect is appreciable and can be modified by polarization to give an effect, similar to piezoelectricity, called the ferroelectric effect. The output is linear with strain, and changes sign with changes of strain direction; further, as the material is polycrystalline it can be polarized in any desired pattern. Barium titanate and lead zirconate titanate are ceramics of this type and can be polarized by heating them above their Curie temperature and allowing them to cool in a strong electric field.

When used for measuring vibration or short-term acceleration, piezoelectric transducers may be connected to a normal amplifier of high input impedance with resistive feedback, as shown in Fig. 2.26(a). However, by using a charge

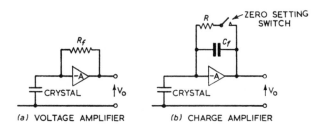

(a) VOLTAGE AMPLIFIER   (b) CHARGE AMPLIFIER

Fig. 2.26. Voltage and charge amplifier arrangements.

amplifier having capacitive feedback as in (b), certain high-quality piezoelectric transducers can be used under quasi-static conditions. The amplifier must contain a very high impedance input device such as an electrometer tube or field-effect transistor. By these means, charges can be held for a second or two to within 0·1 per cent. The resistor R can be switched into circuit momentarily before taking a reading to set the output to zero.

The use of piezoelectric transducers for ultrasonic applications is mentioned in Chapter 7.

REFERENCES

Carter, H. and Donker, M. *Photo-electric Devices in Theory and Practice*, Philips Technical Library, Cleaver Hume Press (1963).

Dean, M. and Douglas, R. D. *Semiconductor and Conventional Strain Gages*, Academic Press, New York (1962).

Higson, G. R. 'Recent Advances in Strain Gauges', *J. Sci. Instrum.*, **41**, 405 (1964).

Ramey, R. L. *Physical Electronics*, Wadsworth Publishing Co. Inc., Belmont, Calif. (1961).

Seel, F. *Atomic Structure and Chemical Bonding*, Methuen Monograph (1963).

Sisler, H. H. *Electronic Structure, Properties and the Periodic Law*, Reinhold Publishing Corporation, New York (1963).

Ziel, A van der. *Solid State Physical Electronics*, Prentice-Hall Inc., Englewood Cliffs, N.J. (1957).

CHAPTER 3

ELECTROLYTIC SENSORS

This chapter deals with the conduction of electricity in liquids, a subject long regarded as more the province of the chemist than that of the electronic engineer. However, both fields of interest are brought together by the use of electronic devices for the sensing of chemical quantities and for monitoring the progress of chemical reactions. The chapter is divided into three parts, the first dealing with electrolytic effects in general, the second with conduction sensors and the third with electrochemical sensors. The distinction between conduction and electrochemical sensors will become clear in due course; briefly, conduction sensors regard the liquid merely as a conducting medium whereas electrochemical sensors are concerned with reactions and potentials.

ELECTROLYTIC EFFECTS

Liquids differ from solids in that molecules are not confined to a particular location but are free to migrate. The conduction of electricity in solids is by the movement of electrons only, as the positively-charged atoms left behind by the electrons are not free to move. In liquids, both positive and negative parts of molecules (ions) contribute to the conduction of electricity. Positive ions, which are attracted to the cathode, are known as cations, while negative ions, attracted to the anode, are called anions.

Many salts and other substances become split up or ionized in solution, some completely (strong electrolytes) and some only partially (weak electrolytes). Ions are formed when the atomic structure of the ion is more stable than that of the atom. Ionic separation can be thought of in terms of the permittivity of the supporting medium. Since the degree of separation of charged particles is directly proportional to the permittivity, a wide separation of ions occurs in solvents such as water, which has a high dielectric constant. In weak electrolytes the molecules tend to be more stable than the ions, so that less dissociation occurs.

The process of ionization can be described by the typical expression

34

$$NaCl \xrightleftharpoons[\text{neutralization}]{\text{dissociation}} Na^+ + Cl^-$$

In the case of extremely pure water a very few molecules dissociate forming hydrogen ions (H^+) and hydroxyl ions (OH^-). The proportion is extremely small: in fact, only one molecule in every 5.5×10^8 is dissociated, consequently the conductivity of pure water is very low.

Conductivity

The resistivity of a material is defined as the resistance between opposite faces of a cube at specified temperature. Conductivity, the reciprocal of this, is used in preference to resistivity when dealing with electrolytes. It is often impracticable to make measurements with, say, a 1 cm cube of material, and practical measuring cells are made with convenient dimensions and the

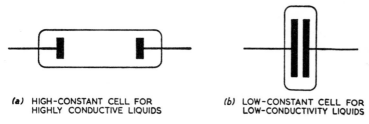

(a) HIGH-CONSTANT CELL FOR
       HIGHLY CONDUCTIVE LIQUIDS

(b) LOW-CONSTANT CELL FOR
       LOW-CONDUCTIVITY LIQUIDS

FIG. 3.1. Conductivity and cell constants.

conductance so measured is related by a geometrical cell constant to the conductivity. If the observed conductance is G mho, and the electrode spacing and area in metre units are d and A respectively, then the conductivity γ is given by

$$\gamma = G(d/A) = KG \text{ mho/m}$$

where K is the cell constant. In practice the value of the cell constant is obtained by measurement with a solution of known conductivity.

It is often convenient to use a cell of high constant when measuring highly-conductive solutions and of low constant with poor conductors, in order to reduce the range of conductivities to be measured. Fig. 3.1 shows the relative proportions of two such cells. Table 3.1 shows some typical values of cell constant and the ranges of conductivity for which they are suitable.

Table 3.1. Conductivity Ranges and Cell Constants

Cell constant, K	0·01	0·1	1·0	2·0	10·0
Conductivity range, μmho/cm	10^{-2}–10	10^{-1}–2×10^3	10–5×10^4	20–10^5	10^2–10^6

Equivalent Conductance

In Figs. 3.2(a) and (b) are shown two hypothetical cells containing aqueous solutions of different salts, the electrolyte being confined to the space between the electrodes. In order to compare the conducting powers of the different salts it is necessary to ensure that the same number of ions is present in each case (assuming complete dissociation). This situation will exist if, in

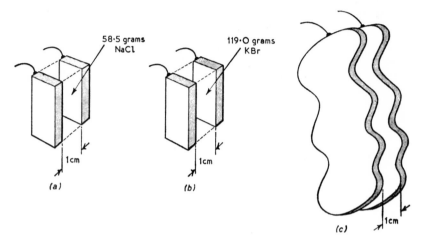

FIG. 3.2. Illustration of equivalent conductance.

each case, the gram equivalent weight of the salt is dissolved in the liquid between the electrodes. The value of conductance, defined in this way with an electrode separation of 1 cm, is known as the *equivalent conductance* and is usually denoted by the symbol Λ. The equivalent weights of the two examples shown are:

(a) $Na^+ + Cl^- = NaCl$
     23·0   35·5   58·5 g

(b) $K^+ + Br^- = KBr$
     39·1   79·9   119·0 g

Infinite Dilution

The ions in the hypothetical cells of Figs. 3.2(a) and (b) have an appreciable effect on each other as the solutions are strong and the ions are close together. This interaction is reflected in variations of conductivity, for reasons discussed later. The concept of *infinite dilution* can be understood by considering that the electrodes extend to a very large area while still maintaining a separation of 1 cm, as in (c). If the electrolytes were very weak, but still contained the gram equivalent weight of solute between the electrodes, then the value of conductance would be the *equivalent conductance at infinite dilution*, denoted by Λ°.

Effect of Concentration

Although strong electrolytes are thought to be completely dissociated in solution their equivalent conductance varies with concentration. This is due to two effects; the *electrophoretic* effect in which the moving ions impose a viscous drag on each other, and the *relaxation* effect due to the disturbance of the total field caused by the displacement of each ion. Fig. 3.3 shows the variation of equivalent conductance with concentration for a number of electrolytes.

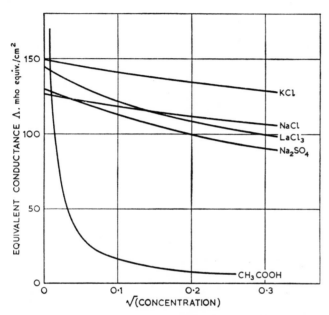

FIG. 3.3. Variation of equivalent conductance with concentration. (*From Hamill, W. H. and Williams, R. R. jr.*, Principles of Physical Chemistry, *Oliver & Boyd, London, 1959*)

In the case of weak electrolytes there is obviously an entirely different effect, exemplified by the curve for acetic acid (CH_3COOH). In this case the more dilute the solution, the greater the degree of dissociation. The dissociation constant α is defined by the ratio $\alpha = \Lambda/\Lambda^\circ$.

Mobility of Ions

In a solution containing positive and negative ions, both contribute to the overall conduction though not to the same degree. It is possible to assign a conductivity to each type of ion by itself although it is not capable of a separate existence. This is shown by the relationship

$$\Lambda^\circ = \lambda^\circ(+) + \lambda^\circ(-)$$

Where $\lambda°(+)$ and $\lambda°(-)$ are the *equivalent ionic conductances* of the cation and anion respectively. The proportion of current carried by any particular ion is known as the transport number.

Table 3.2 shows the equivalent ionic conductances for a number of common electrolytes at infinite dilution. The fact that different ions, carrying the same charge and under the influence of the same electric field, have differing conductances is due to their differing mobilities. Ions move quite slowly through an electrolyte, a typical linear velocity being of the order of 10^{-3} cm/s with an electric field of 1 V/cm.

Table 3.2. Equivalent Ionic Conductances at 25°C and Infinite Dilution
(*Data from Kortüm, G.* Treatise on Electrochemistry, *Elsevier, 1965*)

Cations	$\lambda(+)$	Anions	$\lambda(-)$
H^+	349·8	OH^-	198·6
Na^+	50·10	Cl^-	76·3
K^+	73·50	Br^-	78·14
NH_4^+	73·5	I^-	76·8
Ag^+	61·9	NO_3^-	71·46
$\frac{1}{2}Ca^{++}$	59·50	CH_3COO^-	40·9
$\frac{1}{2}Cu^{++}$	56·6	$\frac{1}{2}SO_4^{--}$	80·0

Temperature Variations

A major difficulty in applying electrolytic conductivity methods to sensing is the large variation of conductivity with temperature. The mechanism of this effect is not completely understood, but it is known that viscosity plays a large part. Although ions are so minute, they behave to a certain extent like large solid objects in their movement through electrolytes. Fig. 3.4 shows the proportionate increase in conductivity at various temperatures compared with the value at 0°C for a few typical ions. The inverse ratio of viscosities for various temperatures is also plotted for comparison. It can be seen that the larger ions behave rather as would be expected on a basis of viscosity, whereas the smaller ions are less affected.

Not all the observed effects can be explained on the basis of the movement of ions. It is now known that part of the conduction effect in certain electrolytes is caused by *proton jumps*. An example occurs in conduction by hydroxyl ions. Consider a water molecule and a hydroxyl ion side by side; if a proton were to 'jump' from the water molecule to the hydroxyl ion, the two would exchange identities and the result would be as if they had physically changed places. A similar effect also gives the hydrogen ion a higher mobility than would otherwise be expected. It is reasonable to infer that when an appreciable part of the conduction takes place by proton jumps, the variation of conductivity with temperature is likely to be less.

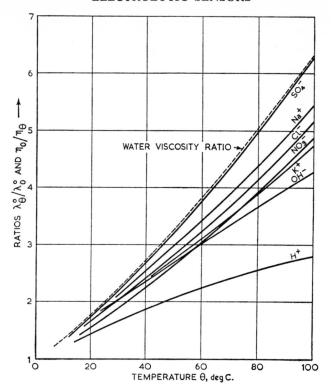

Fig. 3.4. Relation between viscosity, conductance and temperature.

ELECTROLYTIC CONDUCTION SENSORS

Conductivity Level Detectors

The simplest application of electrolytic conduction, and one independent of the conductance provided it is large enough, is to conductivity level detectors. These exist throughout industry in a variety of forms, but basically consist of a rod or weighted cable which extends down into a vessel from an insulated support. When the liquid touches the probe the circuit is completed and the condition is detected by an electronic circuit. Alternating current is used to avoid polarization. Detector units are available commercially which operate on liquids with a resistivity up to 200 MΩ-cm. A limiting factor is the insulator which may cause a maloperation if it becomes covered with a layer of moisture or process material. Details of the application of level-detector electrodes are given in the section on level monitoring.

Interface Detection

Quite often it is necessary to detect the interface between two materials. Provided that they differ appreciably in conductivity, detection can be

4

accomplished by means of a conductivity interface probe. It consists usually of a rod insulated along the whole of its length except for the tip. The detector must discriminate between the two resistance values and more care must be taken than with level probes to avoid disturbance due to bubbles and other contaminants. When working over a range of temperatures it must also be established that the high-temperature conductance of the low-conductivity liquid is less than the low-temperature conductance of the high-conductivity liquid. In view of the large effect of temperature such a condition may sometimes present difficulties. When chemical compositions vary it must be established that under worst possible conditions an adequate conductivity differential exists.

Variable Cell-constant Devices

The conductance of a cell depends on the cell constant K, and a simple means of sensing is available whereby physical movements are converted into changes of cell shape or dimension. Gramophone pick-ups have been constructed on this principle in which the vibrations of the stylus are transmitted as variations of thickness of an electrolyte path. The method is capable of wide application and two examples follow.

The Dracone Strain-gauge. The Dracone itself is a flexible barge developed by Dracone Developments Ltd., a subsidiary of the British National Research Development Corporation, for ocean transport of liquids lighter than sea water. The barge, constructed of nylon and rubber, is subject to strains outside the range of conventional strain-gauges and a new technique of strain measurement was called for. The Dracone strain-gauge, developed to meet this requirement, can be applied to other situations where large strains, of up to 250 per cent, are to be measured.

The gauge is constructed from a rubber tube filled with electrolyte and sealed at each end with an electrode. Acidulated copper-sulphate solution is used as the electrolyte with copper electrodes. The action of passing current is the erosion of copper from one end and its deposition at the other. The gauge has a resistance r given by

$$r = kl^n$$

for a gauge-length l, where k and n are constants.

A simple examination of the situation, assuming that the volume of electrolyte is constant, suggests that in all cases n must equal 2. However, it is found in practice that n is always less than 2. This is attributable to the fact that rubber tube does not have a completely smooth bore and electrolyte situated in the irregularities does not contribute to the conduction. As the tube is stretched, the irregularities are partially smoothed out and more electrolyte is available for conduction, thus the effective electrolyte volume is variable. The value of n varies from 1·5 with a rough tube to 1·85 with the grade used for Dracone strain-gauges. The value of n appears to be constant for a particular gauge and the slight difference between gauges does not affect the usefulness of the device.

When operated with d.c., currents of about 70 µA are recommended; with a.c., currents up to 500 µA may be used. The variation of resistance with temperature may be compensated by having another similar but unstressed gauge connected in a suitable circuit. The gauge appears to be suitable for temperatures between about −10°C and 80°C, the limits being the temperatures at which the electrolyte crystallizes or bubbles. In some applications it is possible that mercury, with its lower temperature coefficient and absence of electrolytic effects, would be preferable to an electrolyte.

Electrolytic Tilt Sensors. The Electrolevel is a device manufactured by the British Aircraft Corporation for sensing small angular displacements from the horizontal. The general arrangement, Fig. 3.5, shows the sensitive electrolyte chamber. The electrodes, which are always immersed, are in a

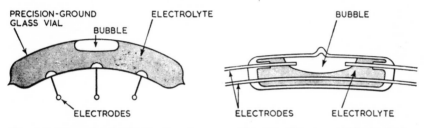

FIG. 3.5. Electrolevel. (*British Aircraft Corpn.*)

FIG. 3.6. Tilt sensor. (*Hamlin Inc.*)

differential arrangement so that as the bubble moves the electrolyte thickness is increased on one side and decreased on the other. The device has an output linear with displacement up to ±40′ of arc, and can be calibrated over the range ±90′.

Fig. 3.6 shows a tilt sensor manufactured by Hamlin Inc. A range of sensors with one basic outline is obtained by varying the amount of electrolyte and radius of glass curvature.

Particle Concentration Meter

When particles of an electrically insulating material are transported in a conducting fluid, the amount of material may be estimated by measuring the change in resistance of the mixture. Care, however, must be exercised when designing the electrode system for such a device to avoid ambiguity due to the uneven distribution of solids through the cross section of the pipeline. For example, small electrodes placed on the diameter of an insulated section of the tube will only 'see' a narrow band of the mixture, which may or may not be representative of the total cross-section. If such electrodes were situated at top and bottom of the tube, a small deposit on the lower electrode could effectively isolate it from the liquid, wrongly indicating to the sensing equipment that the line is full of solid material. A good approach to electrode design for this purpose is the Mawdsley 'Emsol' concentration meter, which has two rows of electrodes arranged in semi-helices as in Fig. 3.7. This effectively examines the whole cross-section of the tube. The conductivity of the carrier liquid is measured in a reference cell which incorporates a filter to remove all entrained particles.

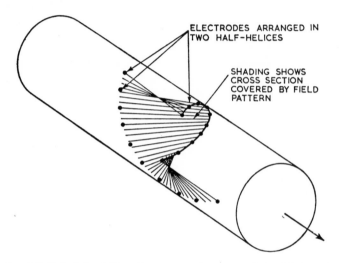

ELECTRODES ARRANGED IN
TWO HALF-HELICES

SHADING SHOWS
CROSS SECTION
COVERED BY FIELD
PATTERN

Fig. 3.7. Principle of 'Emsol' concentration meter. (*Mawdsley's Ltd.*)

Particle Counter

The instrument shown in Fig. 3.8, manufactured by Coulter Electronics, measures and counts small particles in liquids by means of a conductivity effect. The liquid carrying the entrained particles is made to flow through a hole and the conductance from one side of the hole to the other is monitored. When a particle, of conductivity different from that of the carrier liquid, passes through the hole, the conductance alters and the particle is recorded.

The apparatus consists of a glass tube with a small hole in it of known size. The tube is fixed in a beaker with electrodes inside and outside the tube. A column of mercury in a side tube fitted with electrical contacts enables a fixed volume of a liquid to be monitored. The apparatus is filled with the liquid under test and the liquid in the beaker is agitated if necessary to prevent sedimentation. The stop-cock is opened to connect the tube to a source of controlled vacuum; this initiates flow from the beaker through the hole and draws the mercury past the two contact probes. The stop-cock is then closed and the falling mercury column continues to draw liquid through the hole. When the mercury reaches the first probe, the counter is set in operation and counts the number of particles that pass through the hole. When the mercury reaches the second electrode the counter is switched off. From start to finish of a count, the falling column of mercury moves along a horizontal section of tube, thus keeping constant the pressure-drop across the orifice.

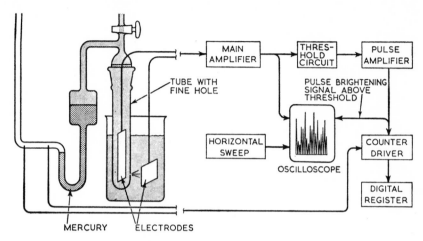

FIG. 3.8. Particle counter. (*Coulter Electronics*)

The principal resistance between electrodes occurs at the hole, and the change ΔR in resistance is due to the passage of a particle through it. Let a particle have a volume V, a resistivity ρ and an area a normal to the axis of a hole of area A; the shape of the particle is characterized by its particle dimension-ratio $x=$(length parallel to axis)/(diameter of equivalent sphere). Then if the resistivity of the electrolyte is ρ_0,

$$\Delta R = \frac{\rho_0 V}{A^2} \bigg/ \left[\frac{1}{1-(\rho_0/\rho)} - \frac{a}{xA} \right].$$

It can be seen that for a given aperture size and electrolyte the change in resistance is proportional to particle volume.

A threshold adjustment on the associated control equipment enables all particles under a certain size to be ignored. By taking a number of counts at different values of threshold level it is possible to determine the proportion of the various sizes of particle. Hole sizes range from 30 to 560 μm, suitable for particle sizes ranging from 0·5 to 500 μm.

Water-impurity Monitoring

Conductivity methods are ideally suited to the monitoring of impurity level in water systems. A typical example is the checking of boiler condensate before it is returned to the supply tank. The conductivity probe usually operates an emergency diverting valve, so that condensate can be run to waste if leakage occurs somewhere in the system and brine or other contaminant is allowed to enter. Without such protection, and if the hazard were severe, it would be necessary to discard all the condensate and supply the boiler continually with freshly de-mineralized water—a costly undertaking. This application is one in which, under normal circumstances, the alarm will never operate. Periodic checks are therefore necessary to ensure that the equipment continues to function correctly, ready to give the alarm and take action if needed.

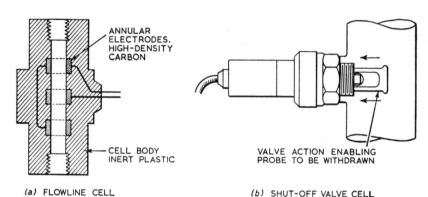

(a) FLOWLINE CELL   (b) SHUT-OFF VALVE CELL

Fig. 3.9. Industrial conductivity cells. (*Electronic Switchgear (London) Ltd. British and Foreign Patents*)

Cells may be of the flow-through type, like that shown in Fig. 3.9(a). This type of cell must usually be removed from the pipework for maintenance. Where this is undesirable, a self-sealing probe (b) may be used. This incorporates a valve which prevents leakage of water when the cell is removed. Both these cells use carbon-graphite ring electrodes and are manufactured in a range of values of cell constant. When the cell is required to operate over a range of temperatures it is usual to apply temperature-compensation by incorporating into the body of the cell a nickel resistance thermometer, which is connected into the appropriate arm of a Wheatstone bridge measuring circuit. The effective temperature compensation can be matched to the cell by adjusting resistors in series and parallel with the resistance thermometer.

As well as for alarm-raising operations, conductivity methods are frequently employed for monitoring 'end points'. Water de-mineralization plant often incorporates cells of this type to detect when the ion-exchange resins need regenerating. The cell can also be used to detect the completion of regeneration. Washing water used by the textile and photographic industries can be monitored for completion of wash by similar means. When it is essential to wash away every trace of soluble material it is inevitable that, unless detectors are used, a considerable waste of time and water will occur.

Brine-concentration Metering

Although not readily amenable to calculation, the conductivity of strong solutions of salts has a highly repeatable empirical relationship with temperature and conductivity. Temperature can be measured and compensated to a fair degree of accuracy by the method described in the previous section. Thus, provided that the particular salt is defined, the conductivity method provides a convenient and rapid way of measuring its concentration. The method can be used for metering the brines used in refrigeration to guard against accidental dilution, which could prove expensive in terms of damaged plant.

In the food industry, where brine is extensively used for curing, it is often necessary to be able to measure the salt content of the finished product. A weighed sample of the product (smoked fish, bacon, etc.) is macerated completely in a high speed fluidizer together with a known quantity of water. The resulting liquor can then be measured for salt concentration and the value so obtained related to the original salt content.

Conductivity Hygrometers

Humidity can be monitored by measuring the resistance of elements containing a hygroscopic material. Either a natural material such as cellulose, or a hygroscopic salt such as lithium chloride, can be used. If it is desired to make a sensor with a low resistance, the hygroscopic medium is deposited between intermeshing printed-circuit electrodes in a manner similar to that used for cadmium sulphide photoconductive cells described in Chapter 2. When a megohm meter is acceptable, a simpler electrode arrangement can be used.

Electrodeless Conductivity Systems

In some applications where the electrodes of normal conductivity systems would become contaminated and introduce error, an electrodeless system can be used. Fig. 3.10 shows two arrangements of equipment supplied by Industrial Instruments Inc. Two separate transformer cores are coupled with a conductor made up of the electrolyte being measured. Toroidal cores are used, the arrangement of Fig. 3.10(a) being intended for immersion in large

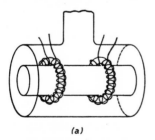
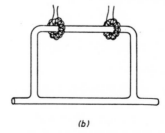

(a)   (b)

FIG. 3.10. Examples of electrodeless conductivity measurement. (*Industrial Instruments, Inc.*)

tanks. The cell constant depends on the length and diameter of the central hole. In (b) the conductivity of liquid flowing in a pipe is measured by diverting a small proportion through a section of parallel pipe looping the two toroids.

Electrodeless conductivity systems have proved very effective when used with solutions containing abrasive or fibrous solids, and with highly corrosive liquids. Typical applications are hydrofluoric acid, sodium hydroxide solutions, 98 per cent sulphuric acid, cement slurry, industrial sewage and drilling mud. Another interesting application is to seawater, in which marine growth can cause extensive fouling during several hours' exposure. The feature of long uninterrupted service is important in systems which cannot be opened for fear of contamination, such as those concerned with radioactive material, or systems that must be kept germ-free.

ELECTROCHEMICAL SENSORS

Two electrochemical effects are now well known and have become part of our everyday experience. One is the production of an e.m.f. from the electrodes of accumulators and batteries by galvanic action; the other is the deposition, in electroplating, of metals by the action of an electric current. The relation of electrical potentials and currents to chemical reactions forms the basis of various electrochemical sensing devices.

Electrolysis Moisture Measurement

This is a method of measuring the water-vapour content of a process-gas system. Faraday's law states that the quantity of electricity required to electrolyse the gram equivalent weight of a material is constant and independent of temperature, pressure, etc. Electrolysis moisture meters make use of this fact by setting up an equilibrium between water-vapour flow and the current needed to electrolyse it. The water vapour, which may be from 1–1000 parts per million of a process stream, is made to flow through a cell where it is absorbed by a charge of phosphorus pentoxide. Two electrodes in the cell, connected to a suitable supply, electrolyse the water as it is absorbed. The current flowing in the cell is thus an accurate measure of water vapour flow rate. Applications of the method must, of course, be examined to see that no other gases are present that could cause unwanted reactions or electrolysis with the phosphorus pentoxide.

Half-cells

As it is not possible to make use of a single electrode, all practical devices use two or more electrodes. However, different types of electrodes have distinctly different properties, and it is convenient to consider the so-called 'half-cell' made up of an electrode and its electrolyte. A potential difference may exist between the electrode and electrolyte of a half-cell, but there is no known way of defining it or measuring it in isolation. A particular electrode reaction, that of the oxidation of hydrogen, has been chosen as a standard and the potential of a hydrogen-electrode half-cell in a normal hydrogen-ion solution has arbitrarily been fixed as zero at all temperatures. The potentials of all other half-cells can be defined as the potential difference produced when they complete a cell with the hydrogen electrode. The practical arrangement of a hydrogen electrode is as shown in Fig. 3.11. Hydrogen gas is bubbled over a platinized platinum (or other noble-metal) electrode in the form of wire or foil. The presence of the finely-divided platinum catalyses the reaction.

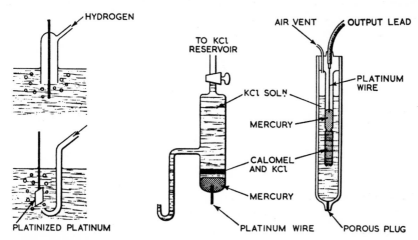

FIG. 3.11. Practical forms of hydrogen electrode.

FIG. 3.12. Forms of calomel electrode.

As the electrode itself, although practical for laboratory standardization, is not suited to industrial use, other half-cell reactions, which have a fairly constant potential difference to the hydrogen electrode, are chosen for reference purposes. The commonest is the saturated calomel electrode (s.c.e.).

The Saturated Calomel Electrode

This consists of a mercury electrode in contact with a solution saturated with both mercurous chloride (calomel) and potassium chloride. The connection to another half-cell is made via the saturated solution. It has been found that when two non-saturated electrolytes are in contact, a potential difference exists between them. This is almost entirely eliminated if they are joined with a saturated salt solution known as a *salt bridge*. The KCl salt bridge is an essential feature of the s.c.e. device.

There are several forms of calomel electrode; two typical arrangements are shown in Fig. 3.12. The p.d. with respect to the hydrogen electrode is given by

$E = 0.242 - 7.6 \times 10^{-4}(\theta - 25)$, where θ is temperature in °C. This rather large temperature-dependence can be reduced if dilute KCl is used, but the arrangement is less convenient in that steps must be taken to prevent the chosen solution strength from varying. For precision work the s.c.e. is often operated at a controlled temperature. The s.c.e. is not readily polarizable, and a small current may be passed in either direction without altering the p.d.

The s.c.e. should have an internal resistance low enough to avoid the accuracy of the measuring circuit being affected by resistive volt-drops. Electrodes for use with pH glass electrodes are not under any restriction in this respect as the measuring circuit is bound to be of high impedance to cope with the high impedance of the glass electrode. S.C.E.'s having a high resistance designed with this application in mind may not be suitable where an appreciable current is required.

Sometimes simpler electrodes, such as platinum, silver, or gold wire, or a pool of mercury, can serve for reference purposes.

Hydrogen-ion Concentration

As mentioned earlier in this chapter, relatively few molecules in water dissociate in accordance with the expression

$$H_2O \rightleftharpoons H^+ + OH^-.$$

An equilibrium exists between the strength in terms of normality (gram-equivalents per litre) of the three reactants according to the equilibrium constant K given at 25°C by

$$K = [H^+][OH^-]/[H_2O] = 1.82 \times 10^{-16}.$$

As the concentration of water molecules is virtually unaffected by the few that dissociate, an approximate equilibrium constant K' can be used, where, at 25°C,

$$K' = [H^+][OH^-] = 1.008 \times 10^{-14}.$$

In pure water the concentrations of hydrogen and hydroxyl ions are equal, and it follows that

$$[H^+] = [OH^-] \simeq 10^{-7}$$

at 25°C. The power of 10 in this relation is the pH value of the solution, defined as

$$pH = -\log [H^+].$$

K' remains substantially constant even when electrolytes are added. If, for example, hydrochloric acid HCl is added, then for the same relation to hold a number of the originally-dissociated water molecules must recombine to leave room for the excess of hydrogen ions produced by the acid, which is completely dissociated according to

$$HCl \rightleftharpoons H^+ + Cl^-.$$

Thus we have

$$[\text{H}^+]\ [\text{OH}^-] = 10^{-14},$$
<small>incr.   decr.</small>

and $[\text{H}^+] > 10^{-7}$: it may be, say, 10^{-6} or 10^{-5}. In other words, the pH value of an acid solution is less than 7.

In the same way, if an alkaline electrolyte such as NaOH is added to pure water and is dissociated according to

$$\text{NaOH} \rightleftharpoons \text{Na}^+ + \text{OH}^-,$$

then again some of the water molecules must recombine to leave room for the increased number of hydroxyl ions. Thus we have

$$[\text{H}^+]\ [\text{OH}^-] = 10^{-14}$$
<small>decr.   incr.</small>

and $[\text{H}^+] < 10^{-7}$, such as 10^{-8} or 10^{-9}. The pH value of an alkaline solution consequently exceeds 7, and may reach 14.

The logarithmic notation is convenient because it is in approximate conformity with practical methods of measurement, which give an output proportional to pH over most of their range. The pH of an electrolyte may be measured with a hydrogen electrode of the type already described; but this is not convenient for industrial purposes. The electrode most commonly applied is the *glass* electrode.

Glass Electrode

The electrode shown in Fig. 3.13 consists of a thin-glass bulb surrounding a silver electrode. The bulb contains an electrolyte of hydrochloric acid of

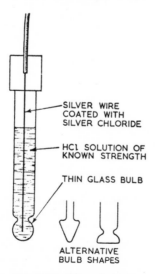

FIG. 3.13. Glass electrode.

known pH value and which is saturated with silver chloride. The potential of the glass-electrode half-cell at 25°C is typically $E = 0.059$ pH. In combination with a s.c.e. the potential at 25°C would be $E = 0.242 + 0.059$ pH.

Early glass electrodes were subject to interference by sodium ions in highly alkaline solutions. Manufacturers now offer specially-formulated glass electrodes that are resistant to this effect and are useful over the entire pH range of 0–14.

Galvanic Dissolved-oxygen Analyser

Fig. 3.14 shows a diagram of a galvanic dissolved-oxygen analyser manufactured by the Hays Corporation and intended for use in boiler-feedwater and other water systems that must be kept low in dissolved oxygen. A galvanic action takes place in the cell formed between the silver and iron-zinc electrodes when oxygen is present. The output is a voltage of the order of 10 mV. When the water is of low conductivity a small quantity of limestone is added to the water to bring the conductivity up to a level suitable for operating the device.

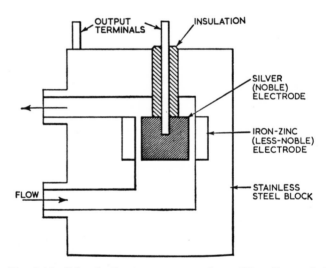

FIG. 3.14. Galvanic dissolved-oxygen analyser. (*Hays Corporation*)

Polarography

The requirements for polarography are a half-cell with a small electrode and an electrolyte containing the ions to be analysed together with an excess of a salt such as potassium chloride. The half-cell is of course completed with some form of reference electrode. When a small negative potential is applied to the electrode a small residual current flows due to the excess potassium chloride. As the potential is made more negative a point is reached where one of the unknown ions undergoes reduction at the electrode; this point is known as the decomposition potential for the ion. The ions in the immediate vicinity of the electrode are then reduced and the electrolyte layer becomes depleted of that particular ion. It is replenished by diffusion from the surrounding solution at a rate virtually independent of the applied voltage, and because the ions are reduced as soon as they arrive at the cathode the current is said to be diffusion-controlled. The rate of diffusion, and thus the current, is directly proportional to the concentration of the ion in the solution. If the voltage is again increased, the decomposition potential of another ion may be reached. The resulting current/voltage curve, known as a *polarogram*, is of the form shown in Fig. 3.15.

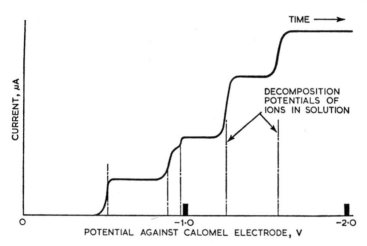

FIG. 3.15. Typical polarogram.

The decomposition potential is approximately the same as the half-cell potential of the ion in question, but may sometimes be increased by an amount known as *overvoltage*. The overvoltage is dependent on the electrode material and configuration. It has been found that there is a large hydrogen overvoltage with certain electrodes; these are chosen for polarography, as the reduction of hydrogen is not a desired effect and it is thus delayed until a relatively high negative potential is reached which is greater than the other decomposition potentials of interest. The overvoltage increases with current density at the electrode surface and is therefore high with small electrodes. When a process such as platinization is applied to an electrode, so increasing its effective surface area, the overvoltage is greatly reduced or even eliminated. Oxygen must usually be removed from the test solution as it is reduced at low voltages and would otherwise interfere with the current/voltage curve. Oxygen is usually removed by bubbling nitrogen through the test solution.

A polarographic effect similar to the cathode-reduction described above occurs when the electrode is made the anode. In this case the decomposition voltages are determined by oxidation of ions.

Polarography Electrodes

The most common polarography electrode is the dropping-mercury electrode (d.m.e.) which consists simply of a glass tube drawn out to a fine end through which mercury flows at a controlled rate. The mercury surface is constantly renewed and is thus unaffected by any electrolysis that may have taken place previously. The hydrogen overvoltage of mercury is high, and conditions are good for the diffusion-controlled current process. Another advantage is that the reduced metals amalgamate with the mercury and thus require less energy for the reduction process. When used as a polarographic anode, mercury suffers from the disadvantage that it is itself soon oxidized, and thus the usable range is small.

Other electrodes, which do not have all the advantages of mercury as a cathode but which can be operated further as anodes, are platinum and gold micro-electrodes. These are usually short pieces of wire sealed into a piece of glass tube. They are usually rotated or vibrated in order to achieve the desired conditions for diffusion-controlled current.

Polarography Techniques

When using a d.m.e., the voltage may either be slowly increased so that it is virtually constant over the lifetime of each drop, or it may be swept by oscilloscope techniques over its entire range during the lifetime of a single drop. The slowly-increasing voltage method suffers from the disadvantage that the current/voltage wave form is not smooth but, due to the build-up and release of the d.m.e., has a sawtooth shape that seriously limits the discrimination of the method. The *linear-sweep* method is more sensitive as it is not subject to the discontinuities of the former method. The sweep is timed to occur quite late in the life of the drop, at a time when its dimensions are changing slowly. A typical value of drop life is six seconds and a sweep of the order of 0·3 V/s is applied after about four and a half seconds. As each decomposition potential is reached there is an initial rush of current as the ions in the immediate vicinity of the electrode are reduced, causing a peak on the polarograph curve; thereafter the current settles down to the diffusion-controlled value. This peak, which like the diffusion current is proportional to the concentration of the ion, is an added advantage in that it increases the sensitivity and discrimination of the method.

Other polarographic techniques are available in which a small alternating potential is applied to the linear sweep. The resulting alternating current is filtered from the electrode current and is at a maximum half-way up the current/voltage step of the polarogram. Variations of this technique employ square waves or pulses to achieve superior results for particular applications

Polarography Detectors

If polarography apparatus is set up with a fixed potential on the electrode then a current will flow when any ions reducible by that voltage appear in the electrolyte. This principle is used in *amperometric titration* and also in specific detectors for oxygen.

In amperometric titration the variation in concentration of a particular ion during the course of a titration can be observed, and the equivalence point determined. The equivalence point appears as the intersection of two straight lines, Fig. 3.16, which are favourably at an acute angle as in (a), or may be as in (b) for which the equivalence point is not so easily detected.

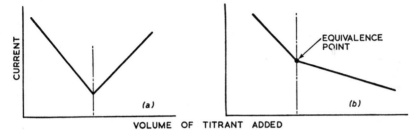

FIG. 3.16. Amperometric titration curves.

As mentioned previously, oxygen is reduced at a low negative potential and use is made of this in polarographic oxygen analysers. There are several different configurations available commercially. One by Beckman Instruments illustrated in Fig. 3.17, is a rugged device designed for space-medical purposes and suitable for a wide range of industrial applications for measuring

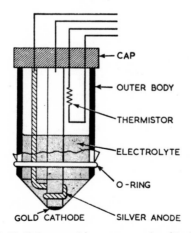

FIG. 3.17. Polarographic oxygen probe. (*Beckman*)

both gaseous and dissolved oxygen. The device is compact, measuring $2\frac{1}{2}$ in. long by $\frac{1}{2}$ in. diameter, and the process stream is separated from the electrodes and electrolyte by a Teflon membrane which is permeable to oxygen and other gases. The presence of oxygen enables the following reactions to take place at the electrodes with a potential difference of 0·8 V:

At the cathode $O_2 + 2H_2O + 4e = 4OH^-$.

At the anode $4Ag + 4Cl^- = 4AgCl + 4e$.

As the reactions are temperature-sensitive, a thermistor is connected into the measuring circuit and largely cancels out the temperature effect. From time to time the device needs to be demounted, cleaned and given a new charge of gel electrolyte. This operation, which only takes a few minutes, needs to be carried out at intervals varying from every other day to every month according to the application. When measuring dissolved oxygen the probe consumes oxygen at a rate which is likely to be greater than the diffusion rate. It is therefore necessary to have a flow of liquid past the probe if low readings due to the formation of a depletion layer are to be avoided. Flows of greater than about 50 cm/s are suitable. Certain other gases, such as SO_2 and the halogens, also have an effect and the application should be carefully studied when these are present.

Potentiostatic Coulometry

Potentiostatic coulometry is a development of polarography where each step is electrolysed to completion. The quantity of electricity used for each step is obtained by graphical or electronic methods or by using one of several forms of *coulometer*. Faraday's law states that the gram-equivalent weight of an ion is electrolysed by the passage of an electric quantity of one Faraday ($=96,500$ C). Thus the weight W (grams) of a substance electrolysed by a quantity Q (coulombs) is

$$W = (Q/96,500)(M/n) \text{ grams,}$$

where M is the molecular weight of the substance and n is its number of electron-equivalents per mole.

As it is not desirable to pass the entire electrolysis current through the reference cell a three-electrode circuit is used, as shown in Fig. 3.18. The current flows between the auxiliary and working electrodes and is adjusted by a servo device (potentiostat) so that the potential of the working electrode is maintained constant, and the desired electrode reaction proceeds. During the course of an analysis the ion with the lowest decomposition potential is separated out first, followed by the next higher, and so on. In this way only one ion is concerned in the reaction at a time. Any polarization occurring at the anode at the same time can often be avoided by the addition of a depolarizer such as hydrazine.

A typical arrangement of electrodes for a potentiostatic coulometric analysis is shown in Fig. 3.19. The reference-electrode salt bridge is arranged to terminate close to the cathode so that errors due to resistive volt drops in the electrolyte do not occur. The mercury electrode-electrolyte interface is constantly stirred to remove the products of electrolysis.

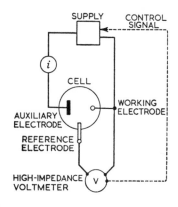

FIG. 3.18. Three-electrode circuit.

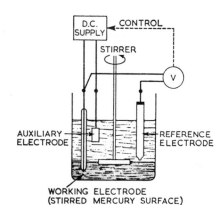

FIG. 3.19. Electrode arrangement for potentiostatic coulometry.

The classical ways of measuring a quantity of electricity are by measurement (i) of the weight of silver deposited by electrolysis, or (ii) of the volume at n.t.p. of hydrogen and oxygen liberated from a potassium sulphate solution. A more convenient electrolytic integrator is the Solion device, manufactured by Self-Organising Systems Inc., which depends on the iodine/potassium-iodide reaction. Another method uses a low-inertia integrating motor connected across a resistor carrying the cell current. Such motors run at a speed proportional to their input voltage and if their output revolutions are counted, or geared to an indicating dial, a fairly accurate indication of voltage-time integral is obtained. An electronic integrator using an operational amplifier is also suitable provided that the electrolysis time does not exceed some minutes.

Coulometric Titration

This is a method of titration where, instead of adding a titrant from a measured source, it is generated electrolytically from a *reagent precursor*. The generated titrant then reacts in the normal way and when sufficient titrant has been added an equivalence point is reached. The amount of titrant is determined by one of the methods mentioned in the previous section. The method is particularly suitable for micro-analysis, avoiding the use of micro-burettes, etc.

5

REFERENCES

Bates, R. G. *Determination of pH*, John Wiley & Sons, Inc., New York (1964).

Hamill, W. H. and Williams, R. R., jr. *Principles of Physical Chemistry*, Prentice-Hall, Inc., Englewood Cliffs, N.J. (1959). Oliver and Boyd, London (1959).

Kortüm, G. *Treatise on Electrochemistry*, Elsevier Publishing Company (1965).

Leveson, L. L. *Introduction to Electroanalysis*, Butterworths, London (1964).

Lingane, J. J. *Electroanalytical Chemistry*, Interscience Publishers, Inc., New York (1958).

Organisation for Economic Co-operation and Development. *Chemistry To-day*, O.E.C.D. Publications, Paris (1963).

Robinson, R. A. and Stokes, R. H. *Electrolyte Solutions*, Butterworths, London (1955).

CHAPTER 4

GASEOUS ION SENSORS

Electric conduction current flows only in a circuit made up of solid or liquid conductors. However, in certain circumstances electric charges can move also in a gas, or even through a high vacuum as in the thermionic valve. A current may also be carried by the movement of ionized atoms and molecules which are positively charged by virtue of having lost one or more electrons. An atom or molecule may become ionized if an electron, emanating from a heated surface or from a β-ray emitter, collides with it. It may also be ionized by collision with α-rays, which are the nuclei of helium atoms, much larger than electrons and with charges of opposite sign and double the size.

Thermionic Ionization Gauge

Fig. 4.1 shows diagrammatically a thermionic ionization vacuum gauge, and although it resembles a normal triode its operation is quite different. Electrons emitted by the heater are accelerated towards the grid which is at a potential positive with respect to the heater. On their way to the heater some of the electrons collide with molecules of gas which is present at low pressure. These may be ionized by the collisions, each yielding a positive ion and another

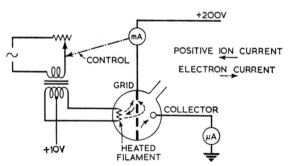

FIG. 4.1. Diagram of thermionic ionization gauge.

electron. The electrons continue in the general direction of the grid while the positive ions move towards the heater. Some of the electrons overshoot and go through the interstices of the grid and make an excursion into the grid-collector space before falling back to the grid. Several oscillations about the grid may take place before the electrons finally arrive there. If electrons collide with molecules in the grid-collector space, the positive ions so formed are attracted to the collector which is at a potential negative with respect to the grid. Provided the original electron current is constant, the collector current is a measure of the pressure of gas in the detector, or rather of the number of molecules per unit volume. The electron emission is adjusted by varying the heater current. In earlier gauges the adjustment was a manual operation, but modern practice is to use an automatic control loop. The control elements for the a.c. heater current are valves, transistors or thyristors connected back-to-back. For use as a vacuum gauge in the region 10^{-3} to 10^{-9} torr, the grid potential is set to about $+200$ V. The fact that the device is sensitive to molecules rather than to pressure, as such, means that it must be calibrated for a particular gas or mixture of gases. Care must be exercised that the heater is not turned on when there is oxygen present at greater than about 10^{-3} torr, or damage will result due to oxidation of the heater. This means that the gauge is not suitable for following the pump-down process in a vacuum system. Sometimes an automatic heater protection circuit is incorporated as a safeguard.

The device is also occasionally used as a detector in gas chromatography. In this application a small proportion of the sample gas is bled into the ionization gauge, while the gauge is maintained at a constant vacuum pressure with a vacuum pump. With a low grid voltage (of the order of 18 V) and with helium as the chromatography carrier gas, then the electron energies are too low to ionize the helium at its ionization potential of 24·5 V. As soon as the separated fractions of organic vapour appear, mixed with the helium, they are ionized and a current flows.

Halogen Leak-detector

Some heated filaments emit positive ions as well as electrons. In the case of platinum, the emission of positive ions is greatly increased if a halogen is present as catalyst. The halogen need not be free; it can be combined in a molecule such as carbon tetrachloride (CCl_4) or Freon (CF_2Cl_2).

An ideal application of the effect is for leak-detection in vacuum and pressure systems. With a vacuum system the detector is placed inside the vacuum chamber and a jet of Freon or similar substance sprayed on suspect areas of the outside of the chamber. As soon as the position of the leak is reached there is an increase in current in the leak-detector, usually displayed as an audible signal. With pressure systems a reverse procedure is used, a quantity of Freon being injected into the pressure chamber and the detector moved over the outside. For this application the detector is enclosed in a housing with a small suction fan and a tube through which the sampling is made. By this means the position of the leak can readily be located.

Cold-cathode Ionization Gauges

When two metal plates are mounted in a moderately-high vacuum a centimetre or so apart, a potential difference of a few kilovolts is normally insufficient to maintain a discharge. By the action of light, cosmic rays or an applied field, a few electrons are freed from the electrodes and these may or may not collide with gas molecules. Penning, in 1937, published his discovery that with a magnetic field in conjunction with a particular electrode configuration the few electrons available could be made to spiral up and down, thus

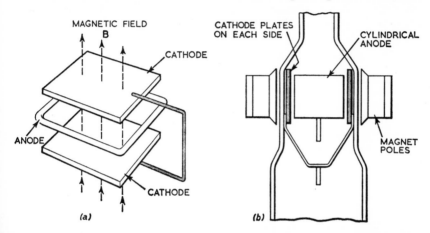

FIG. 4.2. Penning gauge. (*a*) Principle of the Penning gauge. (*b*) Improved gauge. (*From Horst, H. L. van der*, Gas Discharge Tubes, *Philips Technical Library, Cleaver-Hume Press, 1964*)

greatly increasing their chance of ionizing a gas molecule. Fig. 4.2 shows the principle of Penning's original gauge (*a*) together with a more sensitive version (*b*). The device is very robust and virtually indestructible, for there is no filament to burn out as in the thermionic ionization gauge. The usable range is in the region 10^{-2} to 10^{-7} torr.

Hobson and Redhead have shown how, with the configuration of a magnetron, it is possible to use the cold-cathode discharge phenomenon for the measurement of vacua down to the region of 10^{-11} torr. Two variants are the normal magnetron gauge with a radial anode, and the inverted magnetron gauge in which the anode is cylindrical through the centre.

Ionization Transducer

An ionization transducer, described in Chapter 5, is a device which uses the mechanism of an a.c. glow discharge to transduce movements by virtue of a change of electrical capacitance.

Vacuum Photo-emissive Cells

Electrons are emitted from illuminated materials if there is sufficient energy in the incident photons to overcome a surface effect known as the work function ϕ of the material. Thus in order to leave the surface an electron must have an energy of at least $e\phi$ joules. The photon energy is $h\nu$, where h is Planck's constant and ν is the frequency of the light. Thus for emission of electrons

$$h\nu > e\phi.$$

Thus it is the frequency and not the intensity of light which determines whether emission will take place. However, provided that the frequency is right, then emission increases with intensity. An example is given in Chapter 2 where it is shown that blue light of wavelength 0·4 μm has associated with it an energy of 3·09 eV. Thus if a material has a work function of 3·09 eV, light of wavelength greater than 0·4 μm (i.e. green, yellow, orange, red and infra-red) will have no effect. Materials with low work functions are chosen if

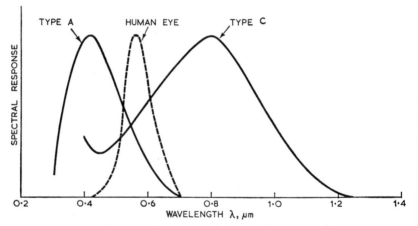

Fɪɢ. 4.3. Spectral response of photo-emissive materials.

wider response is required. Fig. 4.3 shows the spectral response of two typical photo-emissive materials used in photocells, manufactured by Mullard Ltd., compared with the response of the human eye. The type A material, a fine deposit of caesium on antimony, is most sensitive in the violet part of the spectrum. The type C material is made by depositing caesium on silver oxide. Some of the caesium reacts with some of the silver oxide to produce a mixture of silver and caesium oxides. The material is most sensitive to the infra-red end of the spectrum. The response of the human eye is narrower and lies between types A and C.

The design geometry, Fig. 4.4, is arranged so that the cathode is large and only slightly obscured by the small anode. A very small current, known as the dark current, flows when the photocells are in darkness. This is due to a variety of effects including electrical leakage and thermionic emission. Fig. 4.5 shows at (a) a typical current/voltage relation for a vacuum photo-emissive cell. Above the saturation voltage the output exhibits constant-current characteristics, as all the electrons emitted reach the anode.

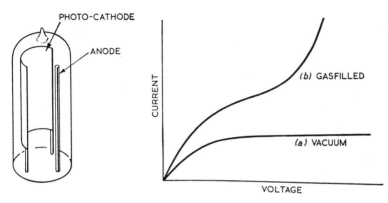

FIG. 4.4. Photo-emissive cell.

FIG. 4.5. Current/voltage characteristics of photo-emissive cells.

The output current of photo-emissive cells is very small. For greater sensitivity two amplification techniques are employed: the more sensitive is the electron multiplier, and the simpler is the method of gas-amplification described in the next section.

Gas-filled Photo-emissive Cells

These are similar in construction to vacuum cells, except that a small quantity of argon is added. An electron emitted by the cathode may collide with an argon atom and ionize it, producing a positive ion which moves towards the cathode and another electron which moves towards the anode. Further collisions and ionizations may occur giving rise to an electron avalanche. When the positive ions arrive back at the cathode they may themselves have enough energy to release an electron from the surface. For correct operation the returning positive ions must, on the average, release less than one electron by secondary emission for each initial photo-electron, otherwise a self-maintaining discharge will take place which is damaging to the sensitive photo-cathode. As the positive-ion energy is related to the anode voltage, there is an upper limit to anode voltage of about 90 V (the corresponding voltage for vacuum cells may be two or three times as much). The general shape of the current/voltage curve is shown at (b) in Fig. 4.5. At low anode voltages the shape resembles that of a vacuum cell. For a given value of anode voltage the average number of electrons reaching the anode for each photo-electron, known as the *gas-amplification factor*, is usually between 3 and 10. This amplification is at the expense of frequency response, because although the photo-electrons are emitted very rapidly on the impact of photons there is some delay while the avalanche pattern builds up. An even greater delay occurs when the illumination is removed, an appreciable current flowing until all the positive ions have migrated to the cathode. Gas-filled photocells can operate up to about 10 kc/s, high enough to be used for sensing the sound-track of a film.

Mass, Charge and Motion of Ions

The electric charge q of a positive ion corresponds to the number of missing electrons, and its mass is that of its constituent atoms. When an ion lies in an electric field of intensity E it experiences a mechanical force of qE in the direction of the field. If the ion is acted upon by a field resulting from the potential difference V between a pair of equipotential surfaces *in vacuo*, it is accelerated so that the kinetic energy acquired is the same as the change of

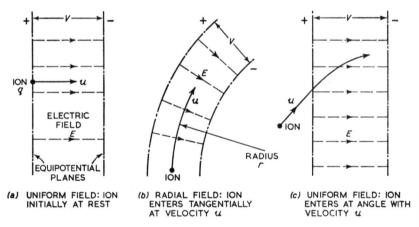

(a) UNIFORM FIELD: ION INITIALLY AT REST

(b) RADIAL FIELD: ION ENTERS TANGENTIALLY AT VELOCITY u

(c) UNIFORM FIELD: ION ENTERS AT ANGLE WITH VELOCITY u

FIG. 4.6. Motion of positive ion in electric field.

potential energy qV of its position in the field. Let the ion be initially at rest and of mass m: then the velocity u reached is such that $\frac{1}{2}mu^2 = qV$, from which

$$u = \sqrt{[2V(q/m)]}. \tag{i}$$

The process is shown for a uniform electric field in Fig. 4.6(*a*). For (*b*), with the ion having a velocity u at right-angles to an electric field of convergent distribution, the path followed will remain everywhere at right-angles to E if the force qE balances the centrifugal force, i.e. the path will be circular and of radius r if $mu^2/r=qE$, whence the radius is

$$r = (u^2/E)(m/q). \qquad \text{(ii)}$$

If, as in (c), the ion moves at some angle to the field, it will follow a curved trajectory. Such a condition occurs in the thermionic ionization gauge, in which ions either reach the collector or fall back on to the cathode surface.

By use of arrangements of electrodes held at suitable potentials, non-uniform electric fields may be set up to obtain a focusing effect on a beam of moving ions. The arrangement of Fig. 4.7 is a simple example of an ion 'lens'.

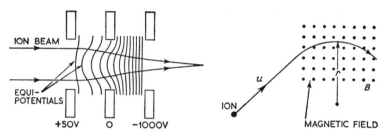

FIG. 4.7. Simple ion lens. FIG. 4.8. Motion of ion in magnetic field.

A beam of moving ions is an electric current: consequently it will also be subject to a mechanical force when crossing a magnetic field. The force is quB, directed perpendicular to both the direction of motion and the direction of the magnetic flux density B. This causes the ion to move in a curved path of radius r such that the magnetic force balances the centrifugal force; i.e. $mu^2/r=quB$, whence the radius of the path is

$$r = (m/q)(u/B) \qquad \text{(iii)}$$

as illustrated in Fig. 4.8.

Let an electric field of intensity E and a magnetic field of density B be directed mutually perpendicular, and let an ion enter the fields at velocity u and at right-angles to each field direction. If the fields are such as to develop opposing forces on the ion, the radius of the ion path will be such that $mu^2/r=qE-quB$. For a critical velocity u_c the ion will remain undeflected, regardless of its mass and charge: this will occur for $qE=qu_cB$, or

$$u_c = E/B. \qquad \text{(iv)}$$

This principle is used in a device known as a velocity filter which can be tuned to pass ions of a given velocity irrespective of charge and mass.

Either electric or magnetic deflection techniques can be used to measure the mass/charge ratio m/q. This enables ions to be identified and is the basis of mass spectroscopy and mass spectrometry. Devices in which ions are deflected by an amount depending on their m/q ratio are known as mass spectrographs. A photographic plate is used to record the mass spectrum so produced. Devices in which either an electric or a magnetic field is varied, so that any particular ion can be deflected by a constant amount on to a fixed collector, are known as mass spectrometers.

Mass Spectrometers

The techniques of mass spectrometry have improved very greatly in recent years and a wide variety of instruments is now available. The essentials of a mass spectrometer are a source producing a beam of ions, a means of deflection, and an ion-beam detector. Ion beams can be produced in a number of ways. Most convenient for a gas is the electron-impact method already mentioned in connection with ionization gauges, etc. A simplified diagram of an electron-impact ion generator is shown in Fig. 4.9. A very small stream of

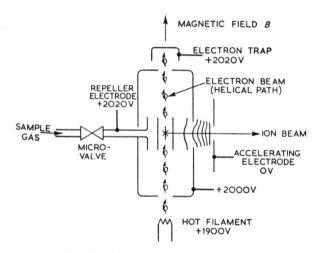

FIG. 4.9. Electron-impact ion generator.

gas is supplied through a micro-valve, and gas molecules are ionized when they cross the electron beam. The electrons are held close to the desired path by a magnetic field applied in the direction of the electron beam.

The electrons actually move along a tight helical path, the axis of which is the desired beam direction. The potentials of the repeller and accelerator electrodes have a combined accelerating and focusing effect on the ions. Other ion sources include thermal-emission types in which the sample is heated on a filament. Under favourable conditions nearly all the vaporized molecules leave the surface in an ionized condition. Ions are also produced from small samples of solid material by means of a high-voltage vacuum spark.

Three of the principal types of mass spectrometer are illustrated in Figs. 4.10 to 4.12. In each case the detector may be a metal plate connected to a high-sensitivity electrometer detector. When this does not give sufficient output, or when the background noise is too high, an electron multiplier can be used. Fig. 4.10 shows the best-known arrangement in which separation takes place in a specially shaped sector of a magnetic field. As well as separating

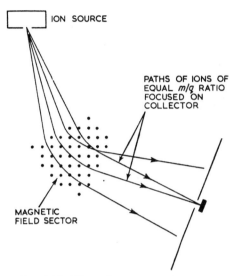

ION SOURCE

PATHS OF IONS OF
EQUAL m/q RATIO
FOCUSED ON
COLLECTOR

MAGNETIC
FIELD SECTOR

FIG. 4.10. Magnetic sector spectrometer.

ions of differing m/q values the magnetic field, if shaped correctly, can focus divergent beams of identical ions. This effect is shown in the diagram.

The Omegatron, Fig. 4.11, is a miniature cyclotron in which the ions travel

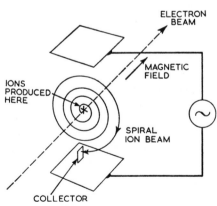

ELECTRON
BEAM

MAGNETIC
FIELD

IONS
PRODUCED
HERE

SPIRAL
ION BEAM

COLLECTOR

FIG. 4.11. Omegatron.

in spiral paths in synchronism with an applied a.c. field, eventually arriving at the collector. For a given frequency and magnetic flux density only ions with a particular mass/charge ratio are in synchronism, all others being lost elsewhere. The magnetic field is in the same direction as the electron beam. The name 'Omegatron' derives from the fact that, for a given flux density B, the angular velocity ω of the ions is proportional to the ratio q/m. The angular velocity is $\omega = u/r$, so that from eq. (iii)

$$\omega = B(q/m). \tag{v}$$

It will be seen that this does not depend on u or r, and therefore ions can be stable with a low velocity and small orbit as well as with a high velocity and large orbit. Besides causing the ions to move in a circle, a secondary effect of the electrodes is the gradual widening of the orbit of an ion in its cycloidal path until it reaches the collector.

The quadrupole mass spectrometer of Fig. 4.12 operates entirely by electric fields and does not require a magnet. The initiating electron beam is in line with the ion beam, which is defined by holes in two plates. The ion beam

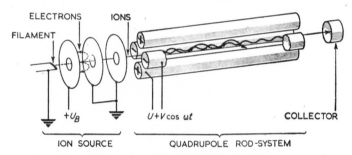

FIG. 4.12. Basic design of the quadrupole mass spectrometer. (*Atlas Mess- und Analysen-technik GmbH*)

travels between four rods which may be 20 cm or more in length. Opposite rods are connected together and a high-frequency voltage applied, super-imposed on a direct voltage. For every value of frequency, ions of a particular mass/charge ratio are able to move down the centre of the space between the rods. All other ions have oscillations induced in them which build up until they strike one of the rods. The current from the collector at the far end is thus a measure of the concentration of the particular ion to which the spectro-meter is tuned.

As well as the three examples described, there are several other configura-tions in common use. Variations of the steady-state deflection type employ either electric-field deflection or combinations of both electric and magnetic. There are at least two instruments which depend on the linear velocity of an ion. In one, a radio-frequency method, the ion moves between grids connected to a radio-frequency source. For a given frequency only one kind of ion passes through in synchronism with the grids. Another instrument, known as a 'time-of-flight' spectrometer, uses grids to switch an ion beam on and off to form a pulsed beam. With a suitable detector and timer the flight-time can be measured.

Electron Multipliers

It has been shown earlier in this chapter that materials emit electrons when illuminated, some more readily than others depending on their work function. Electrons can also be emitted by the impact of ions and electrons; in the latter case they are called *secondary* electrons. Amplification is possible when the ratio of secondary to incident electrons is greater than unity. The most common application of this phenomenon is the photomultiplier, in which the small electron current from a photoemissive cathode is multiplied by successive secondary emissions from a series of electrodes known as dynodes. Fig. 4.13(a) shows one of the several different designs of photomultiplier available. The dynodes are connected via a resistor chain to a high-voltage supply so that a potential gradient exists across them. Just before striking a

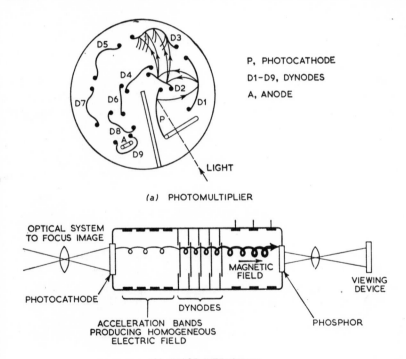

P, PHOTOCATHODE

D1–D9, DYNODES

A, ANODE

LIGHT

(a) PHOTOMULTIPLIER

OPTICAL SYSTEM TO FOCUS IMAGE

MAGNETIC FIELD

VIEWING DEVICE

PHOTOCATHODE

DYNODES

ACCELERATION BANDS PRODUCING HOMOGENEOUS ELECTRIC FIELD

PHOSPHOR

(b) IMAGE INTENSIFIER

FIG. 4.13. Two examples of photomultiplication. (a) *RCA 931-A*. (b) *20th Century Electronics Ltd*.

dynode an electron comes under the influence of the potential of the next dynode which is intended to capture the secondary electrons. Care must be taken in the design that this potential does not appreciably deflect the incident electrons. Precise shaping and angling is necessary so that all electrons strike their correct targets. Gains of more than 10^8 are possible, but the requirement for a high-voltage supply of the order of 1–2 kV limits the use of the device to those applications where its high sensitivity is essential. Another photo-multiplier is the 'venetian-blind' type, in which the dynodes resemble the slats of a venetian blind.

In the image intensifier, Fig. 4.13(b), the path of the electrons between dynodes is controlled by the combined action of homogeneous coaxial electric and magnetic fields. The image to be intensified is focused on to the photocathode by an optical lens and an equivalent photoelectron image is produced inside the tube. Any electrons which happen to be emitted along the axis of the tube are unaffected by the magnetic field and strike the first dynode at the correct image point. All other electrons are emitted at an angle to the axis and consequently move in a helix under the combined effect of the electric and magnetic fields. After each complete loop of the helix all the electrons arrive back at the correct image point. Further focused images are produced after two, three or more complete loops described by the electrons during transit. The potentials are so adjusted that a focused electron image falls on each dynode. The average stage-gain is about five, corresponding to an overall electron gain of 3000.

Electron multipliers are also used in mass spectrometry as sensitive ion-beam detectors. A novel design, due to Goodrich and Wiley, is the resistance-strip magnetic multiplier shown in Fig. 4.14. Incident ions pass through the grid and strike the cathode producing electrons; these move in a curved path under the influence of a magnetic field (perpendicular to the plane of the diagram) until they strike the dynode strip. This strip is of high-resistance material and is used in conjunction with a similar strip at the top to produce

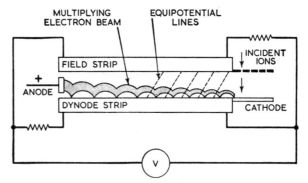

FIG. 4.14. Resistance strip magnetic multiplier. (*Goodrich & Wiley*)

sloping equipotential planes. The effect is similar to that of discrete dynodes of more conventional designs in that an increasing electron beam builds up for each incident particle. A particular advantage of this design over the conventional one, for mass spectrometry, is that the device is not affected by periodic exposure to air. Current gains of up to 10^7 have been obtained.

An important use for photoelectric electron multiplier tubes is in conjunction with a scintillating material for detection of radioactive particles and radiation. This application is mentioned in Chapter 7.

Ionization Currents and Voltages

If a gas discharge tube having a thin wire anode is subjected to the action of α-rays or β-rays, current pulses will flow in the circuit depending on the voltage applied. Fig. 4.15 illustrates the effect for various ranges of anode

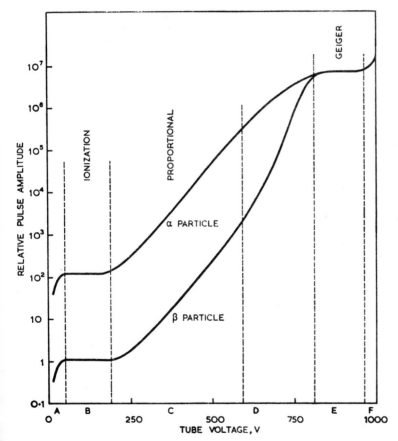

FIG. 4.15. Ionization regions. (*From Horst, H. L. van der*, Gas Discharge Tubes, *Philips Technical Library, Cleaver-Hume Press, 1964*)

voltage. It can be seen that several well-defined operating regions exist, labelled A to F.

In region A the applied voltage is so low that some of the ions recombine before reaching an electrode. The region is of little use for sensing. In region B, the *saturation region*, ionization of each incident particle contributes to the main current, which is independent of the applied voltage. Ions neither recombine nor cause any multiplication effect. This region is used in detecting radiation particles, detection in gas chromatography, and in measurement of vacuum pressures.

In region C, the *proportional region*, a controlled amount of avalanche multiplication occurs. With thin wire anodes the field is greatest in the region of the anode and the initial ionization usually occurs there. The current/voltage relationship is such that log (current) is proportional to increase of anode voltage. When used for detecting X-rays, a gas such as argon is included to absorb the X-ray energy. In the region D, of *limited proportionality*, similar effects occur but are no longer subject to the logarithmic law.

In region E, the *Geiger region*, the size of the current pulse is independent of the initiating particle even though the ionizing effect of α-particles is vastly greater than that of β-particles. The pulse current increases linearly with the anode voltage. Above region E, spurious discharges may take place leading to complete breakdown. The practical application of the various regions to sensing is now considered.

Radioactive Particle and Radiation Detectors

Regions B, C and E above are all used for sensing radioactive particles and radiation. Region B, the region of the ionization chamber, is of course the least sensitive, as no multiplication process occurs. Ionization chambers are basically simple devices, consisting of two electrodes sealed in an envelope with a suitable gas filling. The only complexity arises in connection with the extremely high insulation resistance required if the weak output is not to be lost. Under good conditions an ionization chamber is able to resolve an individual α particle, giving a pulse output just discernible above the noise level. The sensitivity to β particles is small because very little of their energy is lost by ionization during transit of the tube; however, a useful mean current is obtained. By the addition of a gas such as argon to absorb X-rays the device is made sensitive to them, but the sensitivity is low. For the detection of neutrons (which, being uncharged, do not themselves produce ionization) a suitable neutron-sensitive material must be included within the envelope. One or both electrodes may be coated with the material.

Fig. 4.16 shows a tube intended for operation in the proportional region C. The tube is filled with xenon and methane, the xenon giving sensitivity to X-rays. The anode in the example shown is a very fine wire, and only a small region round it is sensitive to radiation. X-rays are admitted through a mica window and absorbed by xenon away from the sensitive region, the ionization then being achieved by a secondary effect. Neutron-sensitive materials are also incorporated in proportional counters for neutron detection.

The most well-known radiation detector is the Geiger counter in which, as mentioned above, the output is independent of the kind of particle being detected. Whenever a discharge is initiated by a particle at some point along the anode, it is propagated very rapidly to all parts of the anode by ultra-violet radiation, thus a standardized pulse is obtained. The discharge is then

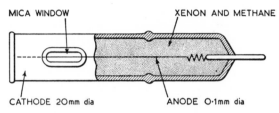

FIG. 4.16. Proportional counter tube. (*Philips type 18511*)

extinguished so that further particles may be detected. A number of mechanisms operate to achieve this effect; one is that a space charge builds up round the anode so tending to inhibit further ionization. In some tubes, known as the self-quenched variety, a small quantity of an organic gas or halogen is added which absorbs the ionization energy and does not itself give rise to secondary emission. Where an organic gas is used it gradually gets used up as the effect is not reversible. A limited life, of the order of 10^8 counts, has therefore to be assigned to the tube. The halogen effect is reversible and so a much greater tube life is obtained. In tubes that do not incorporate a quenching gas some means has to be provided in the associated electronic equipment to lower the tube voltage after each pulse. Fig. 4.17 shows two modern halogen-quenched Geiger tubes. The needle probe, although intended primarily for medical applications, could well prove useful in instrumentation and research.

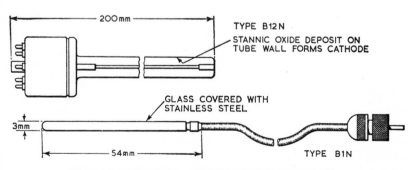

FIG. 4.17. Geiger tubes. (*20th Century Electronics Ltd.*)

6

Ionization Detectors for Gas Chromatography

A number of detectors used in gas chromatography employ the kind of ionization represented by region B of Fig. 4.15. These are the ionization cross-section detector, the argon detector, the electron-capture ionization detector, and the flame ionization detector.

The *cross-section detector* is so called because large molecules, with large cross-sectional area, are more likely to be hit and ionized by an electron than are small molecules. Fig. 4.18 shows the general arrangement in schematic form. The source of ionizing radiation is usually in the form of foil fixed to the inside of the chamber. As α particles have such a short range in air, a more energetic β particle emitter is required such as Sr^{90}. The potential applied is of the order of 500 V and a current of the order of 0·01 μA is obtained. Hydrogen and helium are suitable carrier gases for use with this detector as their ionization is low, minimizing the background current.

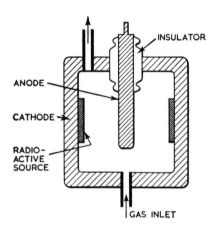

FIG. 4.18. Cross-section ionization detector.

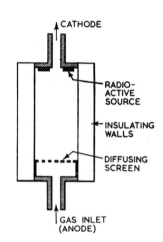

FIG. 4.19. Electron-capture ionization detector.

The *argon detector* depends on the metastable properties of the rare gases. When an ionizing particle or quantum of energy strikes an argon atom it may go into an excited but non-ionized state corresponding to the raising of an electron to a higher energy level. With most atoms, the time spent in an excited state is very short indeed, of the order of 10^{-8} sec, but with the rare gases it is of the order of 10^{-4} sec. Excited rare gas atoms are therefore said to be in a metastable state. The excitation energy of argon is greater than the ionization energy of most organic molecules so when hit by a metastable argon atom, an organic molecule is ionized. In this way a very sensitive detector can be constructed. The background current is very small as the metastable atoms make no contribution. The arrangement of Fig. 4.18 can be used as an argon detector, although improved designs have been described and are commercially available.

The *electron-capture ionization detector* is used for detecting halogenated compounds and depends on (i) the great affinity of the halogens for free electrons, and (ii) on the fact that positive and negative molecular ions are much more likely to recombine than are free electrons and positive ions. Thus halogens do all they can to get an electron but, having done so, become a ready target for neutralization by positive ions. Fig. 4.19 shows diagrammatically a possible form of electron-capture detector. The polarity is such that electrons formed by ionization at one end are drawn towards the anode against the gas stream. When no halogen compound is present the potential is adjusted so that an appreciable current flows. The presence of a halogenated compound in the carrier gas then causes a reduction of anode current.

The *flame-ionization detector* has become very important in gas chromatography. Hydrogen is used either as the carrier gas or introduced just before the detector to provide the burning gas. The conductivity of the flame is measured between a platinum jet at a positive potential and a block of platinum gauze which acts as the negative electrode. The device is simple, rugged and stable in performance. Most organic gases respond, and all hydrocarbons. On the other hand the detector is insensitive to water vapour. It is necessary to calibrate for each expected compound as the sensitivity varies from one compound to another.

Alpha-ray Vacuum Gauge

The ionization of air and other gases by α rays provides a means of measuring pressure in vacuum systems. A chamber similar to that in Fig. 4.18 is used with a potential of the order of 300 V. The gauge is not damaged by air at atmospheric pressure; in fact, it will operate as a pressure gauge at pressures slightly above atmospheric. In the low-pressure region the gauge is useful down to 10^{-3} or 10^{-4} torr.

REFERENCES

Blanchard, C. H., Burnett, C. R., Stoner, R. G. and Weber, R. G. *Introduction to Modern Physics*, Prentice-Hall Inc., Englewood Cliffs, N.J. (1959).

Goodrich, G. W. and Wiley, W. C. 'Resistance Strip Magnetic Electron Multiplier', *Rev. Sci. Instr.* **32**, 846 (1961); see also *Rev. Sci. Instr.* **33**, 761 (1962).

Hobson, J. P. and Redhead, P. A. 'Operation of an inverted magnetron in the pressure range 10^{-3} to 10^{-12} mmHg', *Canad. J. Phys.*, **36**, 271 (1958).

Horst, H. L. van der. *Gas Discharge Tubes*, Philips Technical Library, Cleaver-Hume Press Ltd. (1964).

McDowell, C. A., (ed.). *Mass Spectrometry*, McGraw-Hill (1963).

Ramey, R. L. *Physical Electronics*, Wadsworth Publishing Company, Inc., Belmont, Calif. (1961).

Thomson J. and Callick, E. B. *Electron Physics and Technology*, English Universities Press (1959).

CHAPTER 5

CAPACITIVE SENSORS

As an electrical capacitor is such a simple device it would seem to offer an easy solution to many measurement problems. However, the application of capacitive methods requires careful attention to detail, both in the mechanical arrangement and in the electrical circuitry. Simplicity is often lost in the complexity of the measuring circuit. In general capacitive sensing methods are employed only when others have been tried and found wanting.

Electrode Configurations

The two commonest electrode configurations for capacitors are the parallel and concentric arrangements. Fig. 5.1(a) shows an elementary parallel-plate capacitor, and it can be seen that the electric lines of force in the centre region are parallel. Movement of the capacitor plates in the direction of these lines of force changes the capacitance inversely as the plate spacing. The fringing effect where the lines of force bend outwards at the edges is obviously not conducive to accurate measurement. In order to reduce this effect the uniform and non-uniform portions of the field can be separated by surrounding one of the electrodes with a guard ring, as in Fig. 5.1(b). This guard ring must then be driven so as to follow the main electrode with regard to voltage and phase.

The capacitance of a guarded capacitor, comprising parallel electrodes

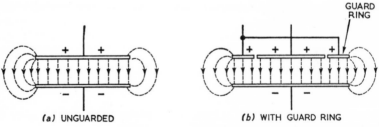

(a) UNGUARDED   (b) WITH GUARD RING

FIG. 5.1. Use of a guard ring.

74

spaced d apart, with an active main electrode of area A, and immersed in a dielectric medium of absolute permittivity $\epsilon = \epsilon_r \epsilon_0$, is

$$C = \epsilon_r \epsilon_0 (A/d) = 8{\cdot}854 \times 10^{-12} \epsilon_r (A/d) \text{ farad}$$

where ϵ_r is the relative permittivity (or 'dielectric constant'), ϵ_0 is the absolute permittivity of free space ($\simeq 1/36\pi \times 10^9$), and all dimensions are in terms of metres.

The concentric capacitor has the important property that its capacitance is, to the first order of magnitude, independent of small eccentricities of the axis of the central electrode. This makes it suitable for measurements involving variations of the dielectric, as less precision of spacing is required than would be with a parallel-plate capacitor.

Another electrode configuration sometimes used employs fringing fields for measurement in a plane. An example of its application to the measurement of moisture in sheet materials is given later in this chapter.

Dielectrics

In simple cases where the space between electrodes is filled with a non-conducting medium the capacitance is, by definition, obtained by multiplying the value of an equivalent air-spaced capacitor by the relative permittivity of the material. Quite frequently, however, the space between electrodes is

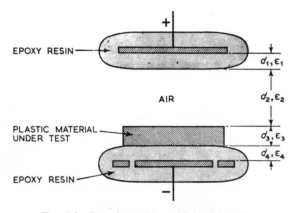

FIG. 5.2. Capacitor with multiple dielectrics.

occupied by a number of different materials and the resulting capacitance will depend on the properties of them all. For example, Fig. 5.2 shows a typical case where the dielectric space contains epoxy resin, air and a block of plastic material. We can derive the total capacitance by considering the situation that would exist if a thin metal foil were placed at each dielectric interface. As each foil would be perpendicular to the lines of force, and thus in an equipotential plane, it would not disturb the electrical field; hence the capacitance would remain unchanged. The total capacitance can then be considered as being made up of a number of smaller capacitors in series formed between the foil layers, i.e.

$$C = 1/[(1/C_1)+(1/C_2)+(1/C_3)].$$

Quite frequently the dielectric material also has conducting properties. At low frequencies the material may appear to be resistive while at high frequencies the capacitive effect is predominant.

Operating Frequencies

The frequency chosen for capacitive sensing equipment is often a compromise. At normal supply frequencies, while there is a ready-made and cheap source of power available, the capacitances involved represent such high impedances that any advantage is lost by the need to provide high-gain amplifiers in the measuring or detector circuits. At audio frequencies, useful improvement in signal level is obtained, accurately-wound transformers can be constructed, and stray capacitance effects can be minimized. An audio frequency often used for general-purpose precision bridges is 1592 c/s, which corresponds to an angular frequency $\omega = 2\pi f = 10,000$ rad/s. This is done to simplify the many calculations which involve $2\pi f$. At radio frequencies, even a small capacitance appears as a low impedance, so that insensitive circuits can be used; on the other hand stray capacitance effects are more troublesome. Sometimes it is necessary to use radio frequencies in order to make the capacitive reactances more significant than the resistive components of the circuit.

Two-terminal Systems

The simplest types of capacitance measuring circuit are 'two-terminal' circuits where one electrode is usually at earth potential. Measuring circuits of this type are unable to differentiate between stray capacitance, cable capacitance and the capacitance being measured. For this reason the non-earthy electrode of two-terminal systems is connected by a high-quality screened cable to minimize strays and to make more definite the cable characteristics.

Miller-Pierce Oscillator

A convenient circuit in this category is the Miller-Pierce oscillator. It consists of a valve or transistor oscillator having both a crystal and an LC tuned circuit. As the capacitance is increased above the value for resonance, a sensitive point is reached at which the oscillation stops. In the region of this sensitive point a capacitance change of the order of 0·005 pF determines whether or not the circuit is in oscillation, the action being almost free from backlash. If the value of capacitance is decreased from resonance, another on/off point is reached but this is far less sensitive and is not so suitable for control purposes. Fig. 5.3 shows the basic circuit for a thermionic-valve version of the Miller-Pierce oscillator.

This type of equipment has found numerous industrial applications, for example detecting the level of powder in hoppers and of liquids in bottles, detecting instrument pointers, detecting the thread of mercury in a thermometer, and counting small objects.

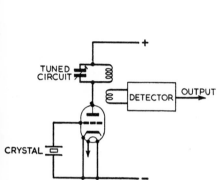

FIG. 5.3. Basic circuit of Miller-Pierce oscillator.

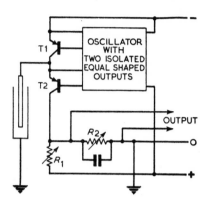

FIG. 5.4. Charge-discharge detector circuit. (*Fielden Electronics Ltd. Telstor 62 series*)

Charge-discharge Circuit

The charge-discharge circuit shown in Fig. 5.4 is used by Fielden Electronics Ltd. in their Telstor 62 series of detectors. The circuit operates as follows: The oscillator produces two isolated square waves of opposite phase and 1/1 mark/space ratio. These outputs operate transistors T1 and T2 as switches. On one half-cycle the sensing capacitor is charged to the stabilized negative supply voltage through T1 and on the next half-cycle the capacitor is discharged through T2 and R_2. Since the capacitor is always charged to the same voltage the mean discharge current is dependent only on the value of the capacitor. The charging and discharging circuits are of low impedance and therefore, within certain limits, the operation is insensitive to resistive losses across the capacitor.

The mean discharge current is linearly related to the value of capacitance and appears as a voltage across R_2, which is variable to provide a 'span' adjustment. The variable resistance R_1 provides an offset-zero facility so that with a given value of capacitance corresponding to zero in a mechanical system there is zero output across R_2. This circuit has found very successful application in level-transmitting equipment, giving an output signal proportional to level.

Capacitor Microphones

The capacitor microphone is a two-terminal device usually constructed to a high degree of precision for acoustic measurement purposes or high-quality sound reproduction. The diaphragm forms one electrode, mounted a short distance in front of the rear electrode forming a capacitor of the order of 10–100 pF. The rear electrode is usually perforated to minimize pressure behind the diaphragm which is deflected by the difference in acoustic pressure between its front and back. When very low frequency measurements are not required the microphone can be polarized from a direct voltage source (200 V) and the signal amplified by a cathode-follower or other high input-impedance amplifier mounted adjacent to the microphone.

The lower frequency limit imposed by the simple readout arrangement described above is eliminated in the Dynagage system of Photocon Research Products. With this system a small radio-frequency coil, mounted close to the diaphragm and connected to the diaphragm capacitor to form a tuned circuit, is then connected to a remote unit by a low-impedance cable which may be up to 1800 ft long. The unit contains an r.f. oscillator and detector so arranged that its output is proportional to the sound pressure applied to the diaphragm. As no head amplifier is required the microphone and coil assembly is completely passive and can be made very rugged. The frequency response extends down to the measurement of static pressures.

An important application of the capacitor microphone is as a sensor in infra-red absorption apparatus described in Chapter 8. Here the 'sound' is caused by low-frequency pulsations of a volume of gas.

Ionization Transducer

The ionization transducer produced by the Decker Corporation offers a very sensitive method of converting capacitance changes into voltage changes. The transducer, which has been described by K. S. Lion, is particularly suitable for connection to capacitive-sensing devices in which physical movements are transmitted as deflections of the centre plate of a differential capacitor.

The transducer consists of a glass envelope containing a mixture of noble gases under reduced pressure. Two electrodes are sealed into the envelope as in Fig. 5.5(a) and the transducer is mounted between two external electrodes. The plates of the sensing device capacitor are connected to the internal electrodes as in (b). A 250 kc/s high-voltage signal is applied to the two external electrodes causing ionization of the gases within the envelope. A proportion of this signal appears between the electrodes due to stray capacitive coupling. As the sensing capacitance is varied, so is the voltage across the tube. This difference of a.c. voltage between the internal electrodes causes a difference in migration of the electrons in the gas, which in turn gives rise to a d.c. potential difference between the electrodes. Variations of the sensing-device capacitance therefore result in variations of this d.c. potential difference. The internal electrodes are connected to a differential cathode-follower amplifier which reduces the impedance to a level suitable for meter indication. Sensing devices using this principle are able to discriminate capacitance changes as small as 0·001 pF which corresponds to a distance of 10^{-8} in. under practical conditions.

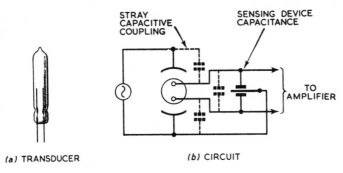

FIG. 5.5. Ionization transducer. (*The Decker Corporation*)

As the ionization transducer is so small it can be mounted very close to the sensing device itself and thus errors due to cable variations are eliminated. No screening connection is possible, however, so the sensing device will only maintain calibration accuracy in a clean and dry environment. A guard-ring connection cannot be made, so that there will be a limit to the accuracy possible because of the fringing field. These limitations do not detract appreciably from what is undoubtedly a very neat transducing method.

Ionization Transducer Pressure Gauge

A range of differential pressure gauges employing ionization transducers is manufactured by the Decker Corporation. Each gauge contains a pressure cell consisting of two stainless-steel parts with a stainless-steel diaphragm stretched between them. The diaphragm is stressed far below its elastic limit and thus errors due to hysteresis are negligible. The ionization transducer itself is located adjacent to the pressure cell within the sensor housing. The most sensitive instrument of this type can measure differential or absolute pressure from 0·0006 torr to 0·6 torr in several ranges. The pressure cell is able to withstand quite large overpressures and its operation is independent of the nature of the gas.

Large-displacement Transducer

A capacitive transducer, whose range is not limited to short distances, is shown in Fig. 5.6. It consists of a reference shaft, made up of a number of annular rings electrically insulated from each other, with another insulated ring moving over them. The annular rings are each connected to tappings on a ratio transformer. The moving ring forms a differential capacitor with the rings over which it is situated and picks up a voltage corresponding to its position. Consequently the position of the pick-up ring can be very accurately measured. As the moving ring is as long as, or longer than, an individual ring on the reference shaft, there is a smooth transition from one segment to another. Devices of this kind are capable of accuracies of better than 60 micro-in. in distances up to 0·1 in. and 200 micro-in. in distances up to 50 in. The sensitivity and repeatability are at least one order of magnitude better than this.

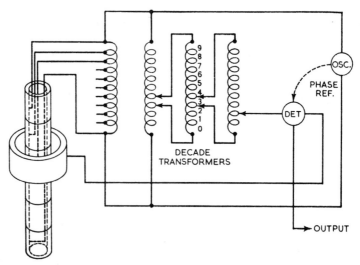

FIG. 5.6. Displacement transducer. (*By Sogenique (Electronics) Ltd., supplied by Societe Genevoise Ltd.*)

Measurement of Sheet Materials

When electrodes are fixed above and below a continuous sheet of material two dielectrics are involved, the material and the air gap. The measured capacitance can be considered as due to the two resulting capacitors in series. If the material has a high permittivity, as would be the case with a moist paper web, then variations of capacitance would be caused mainly by variations of the air-gap thickness. The output of a capacitance meter would then be a signal increasing with material thickness.

If it is desired to measure moisture content, the arrangement of Fig. 5.7 is

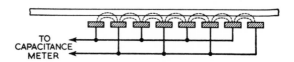

FIG. 5.7. Measurement using fringing field.

to be preferred to mitigate thickness and air-gap effects. Changes of the fringing field are small compared with the total capacitance between the plates, but a sensitive bridge circuit is able to resolve the variations. If the unwanted direct capacitance swamps the fringing field a guard ring system may be employed, using one of the techniques described later in this chapter.

Measurement of Granular Materials

Equipments are commercially available for the measurement of moisture content of materials by permittivity variation. A discussion of moisture measurement generally is given in Chapter 8. The measuring capacitors are often of the coaxial configuration and may either be portable for plunging into a material, or fixed with the material flowing through them. Fig. 5.8 shows a diagram of the Lippke system for measuring moisture in grain. The grain enters through the top and flows to the centre portion, which is kept full while excess grain flows round the outside. The vibrator ensures a slow steady flow through the centre. The electrodes are curved to fit the outside of the measuring tube. This kind of equipment has usually to be calibrated *in situ* using grain samples of known moisture content.

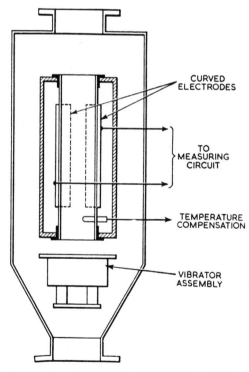

CURVED ELECTRODES

TO MEASURING CIRCUIT

TEMPERATURE COMPENSATION

VIBRATOR ASSEMBLY

FIG. 5.8. Grain moisture meter. (*Paul Lippke, British Agents Orthos (Engineering) Ltd.*)

Three-terminal Measurements

It is impossible to measure the value of any capacitor, resistor or inductor if there is connected across it another of unknown value. If, however, the shunting impedance can be split into two with access to the junction point, then measurements can be made to determine the value of the unknown. This is illustrated for the simple case when the impedances are of pure resistance. Fig. 5.9(*a*) shows two resistors connected between terminals A and B. It is desired to measure the value of X without removing R. Now if access can be gained to an intermediate point along R (as would be the case if R were a stray resistance) or if it were made up of two or more circuit resistors, then it is possible to determine X. In (*b*) the resistance R is shown split into two components R_1 and R_2 with terminal C as the junction.

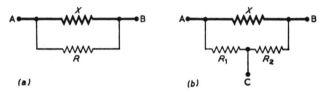

(a)   (b)   C

FIG. 5.9. Three-terminal measurement.

This situation might well arise in servicing an electrical circuit where it is desired to measure the value of X with an ohmmeter without removing R_1 and R_2. Perhaps the simplest way of doing this with a simple ohmmeter is to measure the resistance from each terminal to the other two short-circuited together. If these are designated R_A, R_B and R_C where R_A, for example, is the resistance between point A and points B and C connected together, then X can be shown to be

$$X = 2R_A R_B R_C / [R_A R_C + R_B R_C - R_A R_B].$$

In practice, although it might occasionally be worth while to follow such a procedure, a more direct way of measuring impedance values in the presence of strays is required.

Wagner Earth

An *in situ* three-terminal bridge measurement, now more of historic than practical interest, is the Wheatstone bridge with Wagner-earth connection illustrated in its simplest form in Fig. 5.10. The thick lines are the normal Wheatstone bridge, the thin lines connect the stray resistances as before and the dotted line represents the Wagner-earth connection. Assuming that the ratio P/Q is of the right order the balancing operation is alternately varying Y to balance detector D_1 and varying S to balance D_2. At balance, no current flows through either D_1 or D_2. As there is no voltage across D_2 and R_1 no current flows in R_1. The current flowing through R_2 and S merely shunts the supply and the Wheatstone bridge itself is isolated from the effects of R_1, R_2 and S. Hence the normal balance condition of $X/Y=P/Q$ applies. The need for double balancing, however, makes the method unsuitable for industrial sensing.

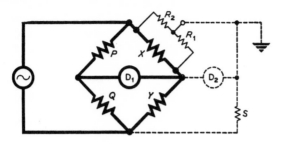

FIG. 5.10. Wheatstone bridge with Wagner earth.

Blumlein Bridge

The major break-through in making three-terminal measurements was due to Blumlein, a prolific inventor, who in 1928 patented the idea of using inductively-coupled ratio arms. The success of his idea depends on the fact that with a tightly-coupled transformer the ratio of voltages across the windings is dependent only on the turns-ratio.

A basic form of Blumlein's inductively-coupled ratio-arm bridge applied to capacitance measurement is shown in Fig. 5.11, where C is a reference capacitor and X is unknown. Z_1 and Z_2 represent stray impedances and it

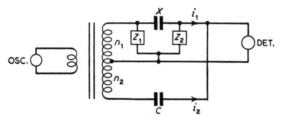

FIG. 5.11. Basic Blumlein bridge.

can be seen that Z_2 is connected across the detector and thus does not upset balance conditions, and only slightly reduces detector sensitivity. Z_1 is connected across one winding of the transformer and reduces the oscillator signal level, but balance is not affected as the voltage across the other winding is reduced in the same proportion. The condition for balance is that i_1 is equal and opposite to i_2, i.e. when $X/C=n_2/n_1$. Another merit of the Blumlein bridge is the extreme accuracy of ratio: an accuracy of one part in 10^6 is easily possible. The toroidal form of core gives the least leakage inductance and is to be preferred for highest accuracy. The two coils should be close together on the toroid so as to achieve the maximum coupling.

Double-ratio Bridge

There is a limit to the turns-ratio that it is possible to wind on a transformer and still preserve tight coupling: for practical purposes about 1000:1 is the limit. The full usefulness of the Blumlein bridge can only be realized when two transformers are used, as in Fig. 5.12. In this case the condition

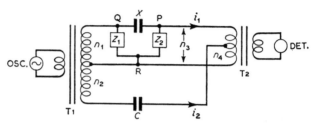

FIG. 5.12. Double-ratio Blumlein bridge.

for balance is that there must be zero flux in T2 and this exists when $i_1 n_3 = i_2 n_4$ The condition for balance is then

$$X/C = (n_2/n_1)(n_4/n_3).$$

As the least leakage inductance is obtained with a transformer of low turns-ratio, the best overall performance is achieved when the turns-ratios n_2/n_1 and n_4/n_3 are equal. If advantage is taken of the practical limiting ratio of 1000:1 for each transformer, then X and C may have a ratio of up to 10^6:1. This has enabled the bridge to measure capacitance as small as 10^{-12} μF at audio frequencies. This led Blumlein to propose a method of measuring the altitude of an aircraft using such a bridge.

As well as providing a shielding facility, the third terminal of a Blumlein bridge can be connected to a guard ring for eliminating fringing field. There are variations in practice as to which point in the circuit is to be earthed Referring to Fig. 5.12, any one of points P, Q or R may usefully be earthed according to the application.

Proximity Meter

The Fielden proximity meter uses inductively-coupled ratio arms and has a double screened electrode as shown schematically in Fig. 5.13. One electrode is earthed and can be part of an object whose position is required to be measured. The other electrode has the double screen, the inner connected to the centre point of the transformer and the outer to earth. Any variation in the cable characteristics between the live-electrode conductor and the inner screen has no effect, as it is equivalent to Z_1 in Fig. 5.12; while any variation etween inner and outer screens has no effect as this is equivalent to Z_2. Thus he equipment is capable of very high sensitivity and stability, and, provided here is no direct electrical leakage between the electrodes, capacitance hanges of 0·01 pF can be measured. In terms of mechanical movement a isplacement of less than 10 microin. may be detected with a suitable electode arrangement.

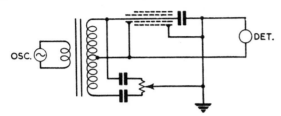

FIG. 5.13. Blumlein bridge with double-shielded electrode.

The bridge operates at a frequency of 500 kc/s, amplitude-modulated at $5 kc/s. Modulation facilitates amplification of the error signal, which may be lisplayed on a meter. Deflection of the meter is substantially linear with apacitance changes at the electrode.

_iquid Detector Probe

The same basic circuit is used in the probe shown in Fig. 5.14, developed or detecting the presence of liquids flowing in process-liquid pipelines. The specification was very severe: the probe had to be able to register as positive vhen the tube was full of a non-conducting material such as oil, and register s negative where there was a sticky conducting layer adhering to all surfaces mmediately after pumping a material such as detergent for cleaning. The probe consists of an active electrode and a shield electrode, with a bridge :ircuit mounted in its head. The electrodes are potted in epoxy resin. When conducting film is formed over the probe the shield electrode in effect makes ontact with the middle of the conducting-film path, thus preventing it from ipsetting the bridge balance condition. The shield electrode is actually separated by a layer of epoxy resin from the conducting film, but at the high operating frequency of 8 Mc/s this layer presents a relatively low impedance.

An interesting feature is the use of a single coaxial cable both for supplying power to the bridge and for transmitting back the error signal. The signal generator is a Colpitts oscillator with the anode connected directly to the mains transformer. The 8 Mc/s output is thus modulated at 50 c/s, half-wave, and coupled into the bridge circuit in the head by means of capacitor C_1, as shown. C_R is the reference capacitor and C_x represents the capacitance between the active electrode and the metal pipe wall. The remaining components R_1, R_2, C_2 and D_1 in the head are concerned with handling the error ignal and transmitting it as a 50 c/s half-wave rectified signal.

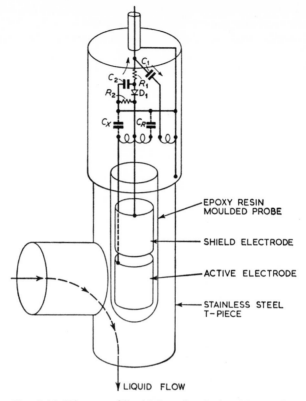

FIG. 5.14. Diagram of liquid detecting device. (*Wayne Kerr*)

Electronic Micrometer

As well as providing shielding facilities, the Blumlein bridge is suitable for
the connection of guard electrodes. The guard electrode will only be exactly
equal in phase and voltage with the active electrode when the bridge is
balanced, but this is usually the only condition of interest. The Wayne Kerr
electronic micrometer operates with a guard ring on this principle. The
schematic circuit is shown in Fig. 5.15. The reference capacitor is a three
terminal device in which one of the plates is moved by micrometer. The
unknown capacitance is formed between the probe and the test specimen.
The range covered by a particular probe is determined by the ratio of the
area of its end surface to the area of the plates of the reference micrometer
capacitor.

The electronic micrometer is operated at a frequency of 10 kc/s and a phase
sensitive detector is used so that the error signal can be displayed on a centre
zero meter. When taking a reading the reference micrometer is so adjusted
as to indicate zero on the meter. Two standard probes have ranges of 100-

4500 micro-in. and 1000–45,000 micro-in. With a mechanical micrometer as the reference, a familiar inspection tool, the equipment may readily be used by unskilled operators. This bridge is able to discriminate distances as small as 1 micro-in. on the most sensitive range.

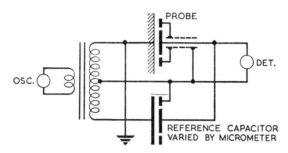

FIG. 5.15. Electronic micrometer circuit. (*Wayne Kerr*)

Evenness Recorder

Another application of the Blumlein bridge is the Fielden-Walker evenness recorder used for measuring the evenness of yarn. This instrument is used with suitable heads for measuring all the various thicknesses and grades encountered in yarn spinning. The essential problem encountered by spinning-technologists is the measurement of weight per unit length of a yarn in the various stages of its manufacture. The standard reference method involves cutting the yarn into short lengths and weighing it. Such a method is obviously not applicable to production control. It has been found that the capacitance of a parallel-plate capacitor varies linearly with the weight of material admitted between the plates, assuming that the material is uniform and that the fringing field is eliminated with a guard electrode.

The circuit of the evenness recorder is basically that of Fig. 5.16. The screens and guard ring are earthed. The oscillator supplies an amplitude-modulated radio-frequency signal enabling final amplification in the detector amplifier to be at audio frequency. The signal can then be integrated over

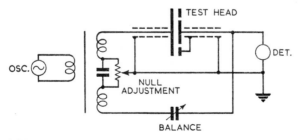

FIG. 5.16. Fielden-Walker evenness recorder basic circuit. (*Fielden Electronics Ltd.*)

7

a short length of yarn and recorded on a paper chart. Study of the chart record can even pin-point machine faults, such as spindle wobble or eccentric rollers which have a characteristic fault record.

Distance Meter

The Wayne Kerr distance meter has the advantage over normal capacitance bridges in that it has a meter indication and output calibrated linearly in terms of distance, rather than in terms of capacitance. The probes used are of the guard-ring type.

The circuit, Fig. 5.17, consists of a high-gain amplifier fed with an input derived from a 50 kc/s oscillator. The amplifier output is in antiphase with

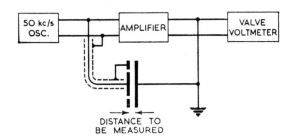

FIG. 5.17. Schematic circuit of distance meter. (*Wayne Kerr*)

its input, and feedback is obtained via the sensing-device capacitance centre electrode. As the sensing-capacitor spacing is increased its capacitance falls, the amplifier feedback is reduced and the output increases. The amplifier output is then fed into a high-impedance voltmeter circuit which also rectifies the signal for display on a meter or for external controls.

As the device is often used to sense the position of earthed objects, the circuit is arranged so that the amplifier output is the earthed point. The guard-ring potential closely follows that of the active electrode as they are connected across the amplifier input, at which point the signal is very small. The volt-meter output is suitable for connecting into a discriminator which can be arranged to give an alarm if the distance measured does not fall between acceptable limits, for example in the automatic inspection of metal objects.

REFERENCES

Lion, K. S. 'Mechanic-Electric Transducer', *Rev. Sci. Instr.* **27**, No. 4, 222–22⁵ (1956).
Neubert, H. K. P. *Instrument Transducers*, Oxford University Press (1963).

CHAPTER 6

MAGNETIC INDUCTION SENSORS

Michael Faraday noticed that, on altering the current flow through a wire, momentary currents flowed in nearby closed circuits. Subsequent experiments soon showed that the changing magnetic field caused the induced currents. Further, whenever a conductor moves relative to a magnetic field, an electromotive force is generated. This is the basis of many sensing devices.

Faraday's moving conductor need not be a moving solid body; it may be a liquid flowing through a pipe as in the magnetic flowmeter, or it may be current carriers flowing through a static conductor as in the Hall effect. As with gravitational fields, the mechanism of magnetic fields is not really understood; however, the effects can be observed and are found to follow well-established laws.

This chapter is in three parts. The first deals with sensors in which an e.m.f. is induced by the movement of a body; these are termed *velocity sensors*. Hall-effect devices are included here. The second deals with sensors in which the induction is produced by an applied *alternating field*. The third section deals with *magnetostriction*.

VELOCITY-INDUCTION SENSORS

The simplest velocity sensors are the pick-off coils used for sensing the movement of magnets fixed to moving objects. Sensors of this type are able to 'see' through metal walls and provide yes/no data on the rotation of shafts, pistons, turbines, etc. As the induced e.m.f. depends on the shaft velocity a lower limit is set, below which the sensor will not operate, dependent on the sensitivity of the magnet-coil-amplifier combination. A diagram of a turbine flowmeter operating on this principle is given in Chapter 7. By using a pulse-rate/voltage converter an analogue velocity signal is obtained which can be used for velocity feedback in servo systems. This is an alternative to the more usual form of tachogenerator which is a special d.c. generator having a linear velocity/speed characteristic.

Magnetic Microphones and Tape-heads

Fig. 6.1 shows the three main types of magnetic microphone; moving-iron, moving-coil and ribbon. The moving-iron type, similar to a telephone earpiece, is not often used as the quality of reproduction is poor, but the other two types are both used for high-quality reproduction. The diaphragm and coil of moving-coil types are of very light-weight construction, the coil being

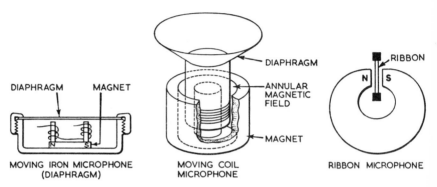

FIG. 6.1 Magnetic microphones.

wound with aluminium wire as aluminium is better than copper on a conductance per unit mass basis. Both the moving-iron and moving-coil microphones have outputs which depend on the rate of change of pressure of the sound wave and are relatively insensitive to the direction of the sound source.

The ribbon microphone consists of an aluminium ribbon mounted in a strong magnetic field so that the magnetic flux density is directed across the width of the ribbon. As the ribbon is open on all sides it does not respond to pressure waves, but moves with the vibrating air molecules, and the microphone output at any instant is proportional to the velocity of air movement. The output impedance is very low and it is usual to mount a matching transformer within the microphone housing to convert the impedance to a value suitable for line transmission. This microphone is very directional, having a figure-of-eight polar diagram. If it is desired to attenuate one lobe of the directional sensitivity a sound absorbing pad may be fitted on one side of the ribbon to reduce sound reaching the ribbon from that direction.

Tape recorder pick-up heads use a simple coil generator, the magnetic flux in the coil being determined by the strength of the elementary magnet in the tape at any instant. The output is proportional to the rate of change of flux and so is suitable for music and most data applications, but there are some special cases where magnetometer-type read-heads are required, an example being the Hall-effect head discussed later.

Vibration Velocity Sensors

The vibration transducer in Fig. 6.2 contains a spring-mass system with a resonant frequency much lower than the expected vibration frequencies. When the outer structure is subject to vibrational movement the suspended mass remains undisturbed. The suspended mass consists of a permanent magnet, and as the coil moves up and down a signal is generated in the halves of the coil due to the changing flux linkage. The two parts of the coil are

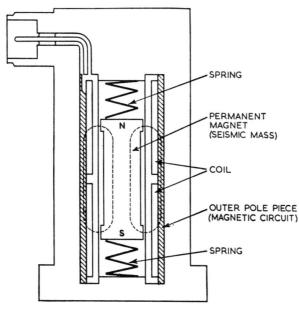

FIG. 6.2. Vibration transducer.
(*Consolidated Electrodynamics Division, Bell and Howell Ltd.*)

connected so that the signals are additive. The output signal is thus proportional to the velocity of the outer structure at any instant. From the velocity signal the displacement (integral) and acceleration (differential) can readily be derived.

The simplicity of the device together with the high output which requires no excitation power lends the device very readily to the remote monitoring of machinery. The ability to detect impending failure in a complex machine is obviously of great value.

Surface-contour Sensors

The principle of the moving-coil microphone is also applied in some high-quality gramophone pick-ups. A gramophone pick-up can be used to estimate the roughness of a surface provided it is fitted with a suitable stylus. A typical application is in the measurement of paper finish. A precision instrument operating on the same principles is the Profilometer surface-finish meter manufactured by the Micrometrical Division of the Bendix Corporation. Instead of moving the surface underneath a stationary pick-up, this instrument uses a precision motor-driven ram to move a sensing device over the surface. The usual traversing speed is 0·3 in./sec. A meter on the instrument gives readings in microinches which can be either arithmetic mean or r.m.s. values.

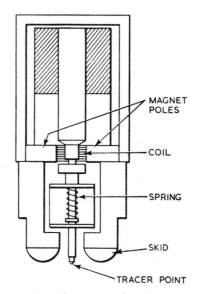

FIG. 6.3. Profilometer surface finish probe.

The moving-coil tracer used is shown in Fig. 6.3. The skid slides along the surface being measured and the tracer point moves up and down following the contours of the surface.

The Hall Effect

Faraday's electromagnetic induction laws extend to the movement of individual charge-carriers in a magnetic field. If a flat conductor carrying a current i is placed in a magnetic field of density B directed normal to the flat surface, then an electric field is set up across the width of the conductor. This is the Hall effect, the generation of a cross e.m.f. by the movement of electrons through the magnetic field. The Hall e.m.f. is additional to, and superimposed upon, the electric field along the conductor consequent upon the IR drop. The Hall e.m.f. V_H of a few microvolts can be picked off by means of tappings applied to the edges of the conductor. The Hall e.m.f. for a conductor of thickness d is given in m.k.s. units by

$$V_H = K_H Bi/d \text{ volts},$$

where K_H is the Hall coefficient, which depends on the product of the charge mobility and resistivity of the conductor material. Metals have very low resistivity whilst insulators have a very low charge-mobility, and it was only with the introduction of semiconductor materials that devices with a useful Hall effect became available. Silicon and germanium, while having Hall coefficients of 500 and 300 respectively (in cm^3/C units) do not find great application as their resistivity is rather high, limiting the current that can be passed without causing excessive heating. Certain materials known as inter-metallic semiconductors have a more useful combination of properties. One widely used is InAs (indium arsenide) which has a Hall coefficient of about 110 at ambient temperature with a resistivity of about 4×10^{-3} Ω-cm.

Unfortunately the Hall coefficient is temperature-dependent, the materials in common use having temperature coefficients greater than -0.0004 per °C between 0 and 100°C; however, materials with improved characteristics are becoming available. For all practical purposes the Hall-effect e.m.f. can be regarded as being accurately proportional to magnetic flux and independent of the rate of change of flux.

A subsidiary of the Hall effect is the photomagnetic effect, in which the current flowing along one axis of a block of semiconductor material is affected by the action of light on the edge of the block.

Hall-effect Sensors

The Hall effect affords a convenient means of detecting the presence of a magnetic field and of measuring its actual value. Figs. 6.4(a) and (b) show examples of Hall-effect sensors used for position sensing. The turbine flow-meter pick-off will operate at any speed, the only limitation being frictional forces which upset the turbine movement at very low flowrates. A number of

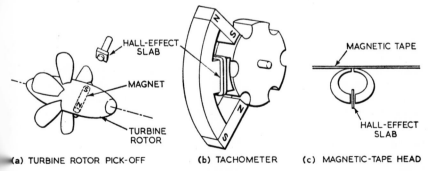

(a) TURBINE ROTOR PICK-OFF   (b) TACHOMETER   (c) MAGNETIC-TAPE HEAD

FIG. 6.4. Hall-effect sensors.

variations of the tachometer pick-off are possible; the arrangement shown generates a positive and negative approximate sine wave with a frequency corresponding to the number of teeth on the wheel and its speed. Fig. 6.4(c) shows a Hall-effect probe incorporated into a magnetic-tape reading head to measure actual magnetic field, instead of rate-of-change as is usual. This is only necessary on certain applications when handling analogue data. The other main application of Hall effect devices is to the multiplication of analogue signals.

Magnetic Flowmeters

As mentioned in the introduction to this chapter, the magnetic flowmeter depends on Faraday's law of electromagnetic induction. There are many geometrical configurations in which liquid can be made to flow so as to cut a magnetic field and generate an e.m.f. The magnetic field may be from a permanent or an electromagnet, or may be generated by a current flowing through the liquid itself.

The usual industrial arrangement is a circular insulated pipe with a transverse alternating magnetic field at mains frequency. The generated e.m.f. is picked off by electrodes set into the pipe wall as in Fig. 6.5.

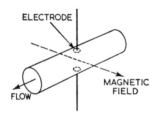

FIG. 6.5. Configuration of magnetic flowmeter.

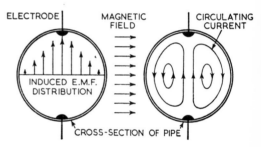

FIG. 6.6. E.M.Fs and circulating currents in flow-meter.
(*Shercliff, J. A.,* Theory of Electric Flow-Measurement, *Cambridge University Press*, 1962)

In the first practical investigation by Williams in 1930, he constructed an elementary flowmeter of this type and made some measurements of the potential distributions through a cross section of the meter. When liquid flows through a pipe the flowrate is greatest at the axis of the pipe and zero at the walls. Consequently different values of voltage per unit length are to be expected at different radial distances from the axis. This effect is such as to cause circulating currents within a cross section of the pipe, the strong central e.m.f. overcoming the weaker e.m.f. at the pipe wall, Fig. 6.6.

Circulating currents cause a voltage drop due to the resistance of the liquid and it might be thought that the output voltage would be dependent on the flow distribution and on the conductivity of the liquid: but such is not the case. It has been shown by Poduska and reported by Shercliff that, with axial symmetry of flow distribution, the voltage is independent of these two variables. But for this the magnetic flowmeter would be very much less useful than it is.

The open-circuit voltage V for a circular pipe meter with non-conducting walls of diameter d and a uniform cross magnetic field of density B is

$$V = Bud \text{ volts}$$

where u is the mean flow velocity and all quantities are in m.k.s. units. With an alternating field both V and B are in r.m.s. terms. In a practical meter typical values would be: $B=0\cdot1$ Wb/m^2, $u=1\cdot0$ m/s and $d=2$ cm$=0\cdot02$ m giving $V=2$ mV, quite large enough for convenient amplification.

Industrial liquids for which the magnetic flowmeter is used are usually electrolytes and an alternating magnetic field is necessary to prevent polarization. The voltage produced is also very much easier to amplify.

The magnetic flowmeter is the most versatile of all flowmeters, its main disadvantage being its high cost. As stated earlier it is not affected by variations in flow distribution, nor in conductivity provided this is above a certain figure. It is also not greatly affected by variations of viscosity, density, pressure, temperature and (to a great extent) turbulence. The range of flow-rates that can be measured is much greater than with any other type of flow-meter and as there are no constrictions or obstructions in the pipe bore it is able to handle the most difficult fluids, even water bearing pieces of rock. The accuracy obtainable varies from $\pm\frac{1}{4}$ per cent under constant conditions to ±5 per cent in the worst conditions.

Perhaps the most important application of magnetic flowmeters is in nuclear reactors, where liquid metals such as sodium and bismuth are used either as coolants or as solvents for the uranium fuel. There is no polarization effect here and d.c. fields are used; in fact a.c. fields are not so good because

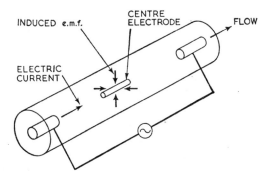

Fig. 6.7. Axial flowmeter.

of the 'skin effect'. Working on the same principle in reverse, magnetic pumps may be used to pump liquid metals.

Other configurations may be used, for example the pipe may have a square section instead of being circular. The axial form of flowmeter should be mentioned. As shown in Fig. 6.7 it consists of a circular pipe conducting a current along its axis. This causes a circular concentric magnetic field. The output voltage is generated between the outer wall and a central electrode.

A.C. INDUCTION SENSORS

These sensors operate by virtue of the fact that the impedance of coils and the coupling between them is affected by the media through which the magnetic field passes. The effect is used for proximity detection and for examining bulk material and metal objects.

Inductive Proximity Sensors

A proximity sensor in which the sensing coil forms part of a Hartley oscillator circuit is the Airmec type N303 shown schematically in Fig. 6.8. With no metal in the vicinity of the search coil the circuit oscillates at about 100 kc/s. As a metal object approaches the coil, eddy currents begin to flow in the object absorbing power from the resonant circuit. A point is eventually

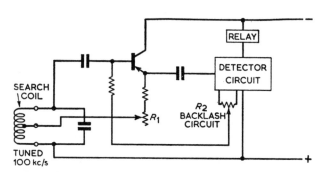

FIG. 6.8. Schematic circuit of inductive proximity switch.

(Airmec Limited)

reached when the circuit abruptly ceases to oscillate. The output from the oscillator is connected to an amplifier and trigger circuit which operates a relay. There are two alternative connections for the relay: it may be energized either with metal present or not present. This enables the correct fail-safe conditions to be set up. A variable resistor R_1 in the oscillator circuit enables the internal circuit losses to be varied and this has the effect of varying the operating point. It is also possible to vary the backlash by varying R_2, which moves the working point of the oscillator transistor when the relay is operated. The equipment is compensated against thermal drift over a limited range by means of a thermistor, not shown in the schematic diagram. The potential high speed of 20,000 counts per minute can be reached if the relay is replaced by a high-speed electronic counter.

The performance is such that with a ferrous material the operating point can be adjusted between $\frac{1}{2}$ in. and $\frac{3}{8}$ in. distance from the probe. With brass the maximum distance is $\frac{1}{4}$ in., with aluminium $\frac{3}{16}$ in. and with copper $\frac{3}{32}$ in. The lower sensitivity with the higher-conductivity materials can be understood by considering the oscillator coil and the object as the primary and secondary coupled circuits. This is true although the coupling is very small and the secondary is only a single turn carrying circulating currents within the object. When the object is of high-conductivity material the secondary is virtually short-circuited and the leakage inductance appears as an almost pure inductance across the oscillator coil, only slightly changing the frequency. However, with a higher-resistance material such as iron, some resistance is coupled into the oscillator circuit and energy is dissipated as heat.

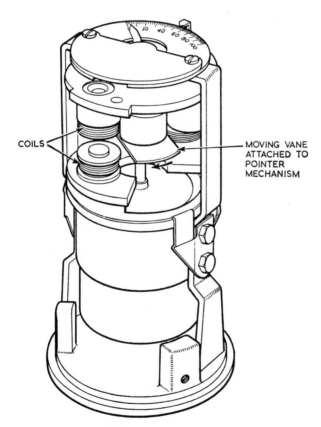

COILS

MOVING VANE
ATTACHED TO
POINTER
MECHANISM

FIG. 6.9. Moving coil meter with inductance sensor. (*Brion Leroux*)

The small moving-coil meter shown in Fig. 6.9, manufactured by Brion Leroux, is an example of the use of an inductance sensor to transmit a signal when a pointer moves past an adjustable set-point. The electronic gear forms a very compact unit consisting of two coils connected to an amplifier, which oscillates due to coupling between the coils. A metal vane on the moving coil assembly moves between the coils and stops the oscillation. The set-point is adjusted by moving the framework on which the two coils are mounted. A d.c. supply of 6 V is required and the output into a 220 Ω load resistance is 22 mA.

Inductive Flaw Detector

It was stated above that the coupling of a metal object to an oscillator coil produces an effect depending on the position and nature of the object. An inductive flaw detector manufactured by Teledictor Ltd. makes use of this principle for testing metal castings and other objects. The equipment consists of a number of coils of various shapes and sizes and an electronic comparator unit. When preparing to carry out a series of tests a suitable coil is selected into which the object can be fitted. The coil acts as the inductance in a Hartley oscillator, the output of which is fed via a 200 kc/s tuned amplifier to a detector and voltmeter. The oscillator operates at a sub-harmonic of 200 kc/s and 66 kc/s.

In operating the device, adjustments are made so that with flaw-free objects in the coil a milliameter on the control unit reads in the region of zero. When a cracked object is placed in the coil the coupling is different, the oscillator does not operate at the same frequency, the pointer indicates an error signal and the object is rejected.

Saturation Detectors

Some magnetic sensors depend for their operation on the saturation of a piece of magnetic material such as Radiometal or Mumetal. An example is the G.E.C. proximity detector type D, which can be supplied in two different sensitivities; a 4-in. head having a typical range of $2\frac{1}{2}$ in., and a 22-in. head with a range of 12 in. The device can also be supplied with two different circuit arrangements giving alternative on/off conditions so that the arrangement most appropriate for fail-safe conditions can be chosen.

We consider first the arrangement used when it is required to operate a contactor on the approach of a magnet. This would be the case, for example, if the system were used to start a vibrator or mixer when a trolley containing a magnet approached a location adjacent to the sensing head. With failure of the supply the vibrator would not run when it should, a condition assumed not to be dangerous. Referring to Fig. 6.10(a), the approach of a magnet causes saturation of the core and greatly reduces the coil impedance. An alternating voltage is applied to the coil, and the resulting current ultimately operates the contactor.

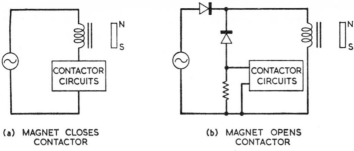

(a) MAGNET CLOSES
CONTACTOR

(b) MAGNET OPENS
CONTACTOR

FIG. 6.10. Proximity detector schematic circuits. (*G.E.C.*)

The opposite arrangement is illustrated in (*b*). Here the requirement is that the contactor should operate in the absence of a magnet. An example of this would be a winch drawing a load up an incline with a magnet on the load and a sensor at the winch. The winch would stop with the load at the top, or whenever a failure occurred anywhere in the system. It is assumed that this would be the safe condition. In this case the coil is supplied with an alternating supply via a half-wave diode. A 'flywheel' diode is connected across the coil to permit current to flow in the coil when the first diode is blocking, and a resistor in series with the flywheel diode produces a voltage when current is flowing. This voltage energizes a contactor via a transistor and thyristor. When the magnetic core is saturated by the presence of the magnet there is no energy storage associated with the current in the coil. The current through the flywheel diode then falls to zero, de-energizing the thyristor and releasing the contactor. If the leads from the control box to the sensing head become open- or short-circuited, the current in the flywheel diode will fall to zero, and the contactor will drop out. Thus the equipment will only close the contactor when the circuits are healthy, and the magnet is absent. Any other combination of conditions will cause the equipment to release the contactor.

Fluxgate Magnetometer

In devices such as flowmeters where the movement of a piston or turbine has to be signalled to the outside of the meter body, the object is often achieved by means of a magnet fixed to the piston with a simple velocity coil wound on a magnetic core on the outside. Such detectors operate on the rate of change of field and do not give a usable output at low speeds. A simple magnetometer suitable for low-speed operation is the fluxgate magnetometer supplied in the U.K. by Smiths Industries Ltd. As a magnetometer the device is also capable of measuring fields as well as merely detecting them.

The operation of the device is similar to that of a magnetic amplifier except that the magnetization produced by the signal is replaced by direct magnetization from the magnetic field being sensed. The device consists of two high-permeability cores, each wound along its length with an excitation winding. A sensing winding is wound round the two as shown in Fig. 6.11. The cores have for some applications been constructed of a magnetic foil wound into a fine tube with the edges insulated to prevent the effect of a short-circuited turn. The primary windings are connected (in opposition) to a sinusoidal supply which may be from 150 c/s to 1 kc/s according to the application. The

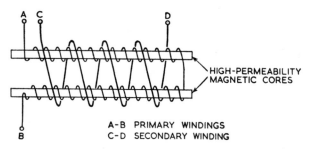

FIG. 6.11. Fluxgate magnetometer.

primary voltage is adjusted so that the cores run into saturation without passing excessive current. During each half-cycle the presence of a magnetic field will delay saturation in one core while expediting it in the other. Normally the secondary gives no output with no magnetic field, but during the times in each cycle when only one core is saturated an output will be obtained. An adjustment is provided to eliminate the effect of slight differences in the cores, which would cause undesired output with zero magnetic field. For some applications a third winding is provided to cancel out the applied magnetic field: the device then becomes a null indicator.

When required for detecting the presence of a magnet, as in a flowmeter application, the secondary sensing-winding signal can be rectified by a bridge rectifier and shaped in an electronic pulse-shaping circuit. For true magnetometer applications a phase-sensitive detector is used so that the output signal is of correct polarity according to whether a north or south pole is nearby.

Differential Transformers

The linear variable differential transformer (often abbreviated l.v.d.t.) is a device for sensing small distances. Devices able to transduce up to 15 in. or more are available, but the main application of the technique is for transducing distances measured in thousandths of an inch.

The device consists fundamentally of three coils wound on a former through which a cylindrical core can move. The centre coil is connected as the primary of a transformer and the outer coils are connected in opposition to form a differential secondary as in Fig. 6.12. The primary is connected to a suitable a.c. supply of frequency between 50 c/s and 20 kc/s, most usually the standard supply frequencies of 50, 60, 400 and 1000 c/s. With the core in a central or null position the secondary voltages are equal and opposite and the output is virtually zero. When the core is displaced axially an output voltage is generated which follows a linear law quite closely over a limited range of core movement, as indicated in Fig. 6.13. There is an abrupt phase-shift of 180° as the core passes through the null position. A small null voltage exists due to slight inequalities in the windings and core. It consists mainly of the third-harmonic of the supply voltage and is usually limited by the specification of the design to 0·5 per cent or lower.

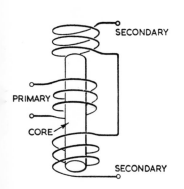

FIG. 6.12. Linear variable differential transformer.

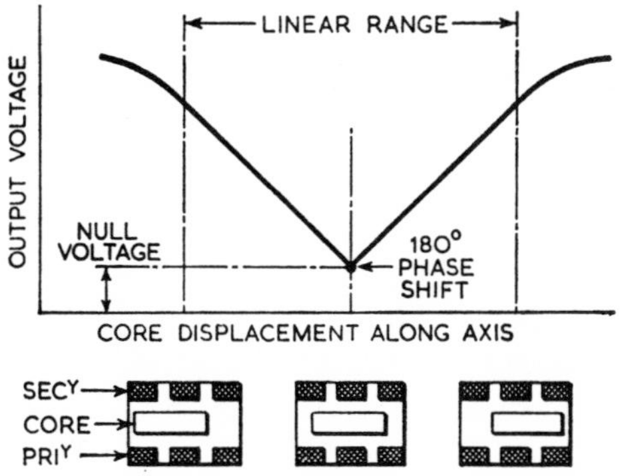

FIG. 6.13. Variation of output with core positions.

The total linear range varies from 3 per cent of the length of the transformer with the smallest devices, to 70 per cent for the largest. The possible accuracies associated with these ranges also vary from ±0·1 per cent of total range for the smallest to ±1·0 per cent for the largest. In the case of a very small transformer of, say, linear range ±0·01 in. and with an accuracy of ±0·1 per cent this represents a linear accuracy of ±10 micro-in.

There are two possible phase angles for the output, depending on which side of the null the core is situated. The phase angle nearer to zero is regarded as the phase of the output with the core displaced in a 'positive'

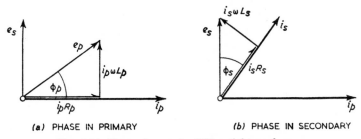

(a) PHASE IN PRIMARY   (b) PHASE IN SECONDARY

FIG. 6.14. Phase changes in differential transformer.

direction. Fig. 6.14 shows the phase changes through the transformer. In (a) the primary current lags by $\phi_p = \arctan(\omega L_p/R_p)$. The secondary e.m.f. leads the primary current by 90°. In (b) it can be seen that the phase lag of the secondary current over secondary e.m.f. is given by $\phi_s = \arctan(-\omega L_s/R_s)$, where R_s is the total resistance of the secondary circuit. Thus when $\phi_p + \phi_s = 90°$ the transformer output voltage is in phase with the input voltage. The greatest stability is achieved under this 'zero phase' condition, as inaccuracies due to temperature changes, frequency drift, etc. are minimized. Transformers can be supplied for use with a specified load resistance in which the zero phase condition occurs at a particular standard supply frequency. For normal purposes, however, it is not necessary to consider this degree of refinement. As well as the effects already described there is a slight change of output phase as the core is moved from the null position to the limit of the linear range, although it is rare for this to exceed one degree.

Transformers may be either shielded or unshielded, depending on the type of outer case used: the coil assembly is usually additionally protected with resin encapsulation. Shielded transformers have a case of high-permeability material which keeps all magnetic flux within the body of the device. This gives a sensitivity of perhaps double that of unshielded types but the main advantage is in shielding from external magnetic fields and in isolating the effects of adjacent pieces of metal. Unshielded transformers having non-magnetic cases may be affected even by pieces of non-ferrous metal situated nearby. This is due to eddy-current effects and becomes more pronounced at the higher operating frequencies. In order to avoid the effect of a short-circuited turn, non-ferrous metallic cases have a slot along their entire length.

Two forces are exerted on the core, an axial pull towards the null position and a radial pull away from the axis. The core is in a position of unstable equilibrium as far as the radial force is concerned, and it should therefore be guided along the axis to minimize radial force effects. These forces are small and need only be taken into consideration when making very precise measurements.

There are a number of other devices similar in operation and performance to differential transformers. One consists of two coil and core assemblies with a movable ferrous armature between. Movement of the armature increases the inductance of one coil and decreases the other. The two coils are arranged in an a.c. bridge circuit so the inductance variations produce an output signal. Very compact acceleration transducers have been manufactured using this principle.

Metal Detectors

The application of metal detectors is described in Chapter 7. Metal detectors are analogous to differential transformers in that they consist of three windings, two of which are connected in opposition, as in Fig. 6.15. The centre coil is connected to an r.f. oscillator, and in a condition of balance equal and opposite voltages are induced in the other two coils. When a particle of metal enters the aperture it acts as a core to the coils and the balance is upset. As the particle traverses the aperture it increases each coupling in turn so that two unbalances occur, one each side of a centre balance position. The phase of the unbalanced signal depends on the material of the foreign body and differs between ferrous and non-ferrous metals. Even non-metals can have an effect, the so-called 'product' effect often observed with foodstuffs. The device must of course be set so that signals due to product effect do not give rise to an alarm. By making the detector sensitive to a particular phase angle the product effect can sometimes be greatly reduced. The particular adjustments required for this purpose depend on the manufacturer's design.

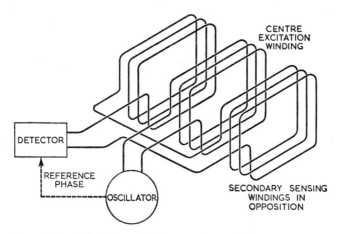

Fig. 6.15. Schematic diagram of a metal detector.

Selsyn Systems

Selsyn devices are used in pairs for transmitting information about the position of a shaft. Selsyn transmitters are of course sensing devices but of a very specialized nature. Fig. 6.16 shows the arrangement and basic circuit. The armatures of the transmitter and receiver are energized from the same a.c. supply and the three field windings are connected together. When the two armatures are at the same angle with respect to the field identical voltages are generated in the field windings and no currents flow in the connecting wires. When there is a difference of angle, different voltages are generated and currents flow because of the unbalance. The resulting interaction of fields gives rise to a restoring torque which attempts to line up the transmitter and receiver. If the receiver is free to move it follows the transmitter. If the receiver is restrained slightly the torque required to move the receiver against the restraint has to be applied to the transmitter. Thus there is no gain in the

8

system and the input and output shafts appear to be joined by a non-rigid coupling. Other systems employ transmitters of the type described, feeding into amplifiers to produce gain in the system for moving large objects from low-power input units.

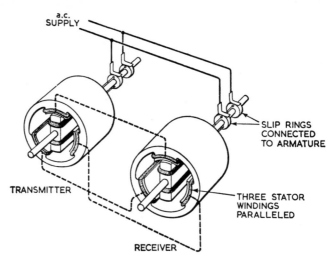

FIG. 6.16. Diagram of Selsyn system.

MAGNETOSTRICTION

Magnetostriction, a phenomenon exhibited by ferromagnetic materials and ferrites, is a change of dimension with applied magnetic field or a change of magnetic permeability with strain. It is independent of the direction of magnetization and disappears, together with ferro-magnetism, above the Curie point. It is usually an increase in length with certain magnetic alloys such as Permalloy and Permendur and a decrease with nickel and Ferroxcube. The effect can be observed in the very simple tension load-indicating device shown in Fig. 6.17, which demonstrates the principle. It is difficult to obtain a stable and linear output with such a simple model, and care in the design and choice of materials must be exercised if a reliable linear output is to be obtained. This has been achieved in the 'Pressductor' load cell manufactured in Sweden by ASEA. It consists, Fig. 6.18(a), of a core of silicon-steel laminations with holes through which a primary and secondary winding are threaded. Under normal unstressed conditions, the uniform permeability provides that there is no flux linkage between the coils, as in (b). When a force is applied the permeability is reduced in the direction of the pressure. This alters the flux lines so that they couple the two windings, and an output is obtained as in (c). The device is available for maximum loads from 200 lbf to 3600 tonf, the difference being the number of laminations incorporated. A unit containing a filter as well as a balancing and rectifying circuit is required as the unfiltered output has a high harmonic content.

Perhaps the most important application of magnetostriction is for generating ultrasonic power. Fig. 6.19 shows the essential features, a rod of resonant

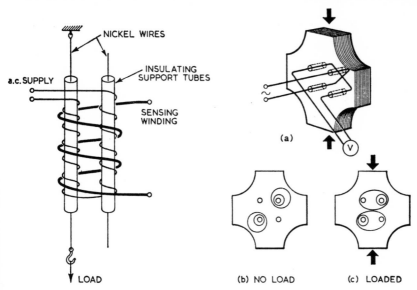

Fig. 6.17. Demonstration magnetostrictive load sensor.

Fig. 6.18. Pressductor load cell. (*ASEA*)

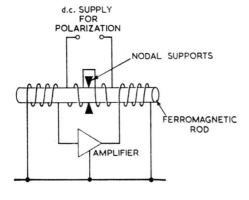

Fig. 6.19. Principle of magnetostrictive generator.

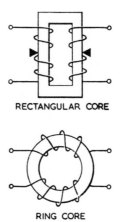

Fig. 6.20. Forms of magnetostrictive core.

length supported at the nodal points together with an amplifier and feedback circuit. This must then be suitably coupled to the workpiece or liquid. A simple rod is not very effective owing to the leakage of magnetic flux. Alternatives are the ring and rectangular cores shown in Fig. 6.20. The oscillations of the ring-shaped core are radial and concentrated in the central area. The magnetostrictive effect is also suitable for sensing ultrasonic vibrations.

REFERENCES

Geyger, W. A. *Non-Linear Magnetic Control Devices*, McGraw-Hill Book Company, Inc., New York (1964).

Neubert, H. K. P. *Instrument Transducers*, Oxford University Press (1963).

Shercliff, J. A. *The Theory of Electromagnetic Flow-measurement*, Cambridge University Press (1962).

Williams, E. J. 'The Induction of Electromotive Forces in a Moving Liquid', *Proc. Phys. Soc.*, London, **42**, 466 (1930).

CHAPTER 7

ELECTRONIC SENSORS FOR PHYSICAL QUANTITIES

In Chapters 2 to 6 the various electronic phenomena have been examined to see what sensing operations could be performed with their aid. In this chapter certain areas of physical measurement are examined from the opposite viewpoint to see what sensing phenomena can be employed to solve specific problems. In order to avoid duplication, descriptions are given when methods have not been described in the earlier chapters.

PROXIMITY SENSORS

A proximity sensor is a special kind of dimension sensor which answers the question: Is the distance less than a predetermined value? Proximity sensors range from microswitches which operate within a few thousandths of an inch to guided-missile proximity fuses operating at a distance of many yards from their target. Most physical quantities can be converted into a displacement and this is often the first step in designing an on/off sensor for the quantity in question.

Proximity switches differ in the force required to operate them and thus the extent to which they influence the operating agent. Microswitches usually require a considerable operating force and this limits their usefulness to the sensing of moving machinery and of power-driven instruments. Reed switches require a smaller but still appreciable operating force, which makes them unsuitable for such purposes as sensing the movement of a moving-coil meter pointer. The various electronic forms of proximity switches require no appreciable operating force and thus can be used in the most delicate mechanisms without introducing significant error.

Electrical Contacts

The most elementary electrical sensing device is the electrical contact, much maligned by the advocates of solid-state switching as being the 'weakest

107

link in the chain' so far as system reliability is concerned. However, with adequate mechanical and electrical protection and with well chosen materials, contacts can achieve a high order of reliability.

The quest for better contact materials has led metallurgists to study almost every conceivable metal in the hope that an ideal cheap material would be found. The relay designer has, in his turn, progressed through the stages of open relays, covered relays, hermetically-sealed relays and then reed relays, each stage offering some advantage over the preceding one. Hermetic sealing does not seem to provide the complete answer as a certain amount of outgassing occurs from the organic materials used for insulation. This gas cannot escape and often results in a build-up of film on the contacts thus increasing the contact resistance. This is largely (but not completely) overcome by the wiping action which is now a standard feature of relay design. Reed switches seem at present to offer the ultimate in contact reliability. Certainly their manufacturers claim them to be the equal of solid-state devices. As will be seen, the truth of this claim depends largely on the rate of operation.

The mercury switch has long been available as a reliable device for switching large currents by mechanical movement. It is virtually confined to static applications as the mercury pool runs to the lowest part of the tube by gravity. In spite of their reliability and current-handling capacity, mercury switches tend to be avoided, perhaps because they are not so easy to handle and design for as microswitches. The mercury-wetted reed switch is a modern application which has proved itself invaluable for overcoming contact bounce.

Microswitches

Microswitches can be obtained in a multitude of shapes and sizes for practically every position-sensing duty. One of their main features is the toggle action, which removes the element of uncertainty from the contact itself and transfers it to a mechanical toggle spring so that contacts are either made or broken.

The following mechanical parameters apply to microswitches and are specified by the manufacturer:

(a) *Pretravel*—the distance through which the actuator has to be moved before the switch operates.

(b) *Differential*—the distance through which the actuator has to be moved back from the operating point to release the switch.

(c) *Overtravel*—the distance that the actuator may be moved after operating the contact.

(d) *Operating force*—usually expressed in terms of weight, the force required to operate the contact.

Mechanisms driven by electric motors can never be brought to rest instantaneously, even by braking, and overtravel must be allowed for. The basic microswitch overtravel is seldom sufficient in itself and a roller may be used as shown in Fig. 7.1 to allow for unlimited overtravel without damage to the

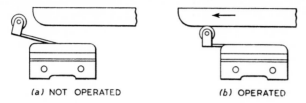

(a) NOT OPERATED   (b) OPERATED

FIG. 7.1. Microswitch roller for overtravel protection.

switch. As well as in the mechanical parameters referred to above, the designer of precision mechanisms incorporating microswitches is also interested in the drift of operating point and differential for any given switch and in the maximum variation between switches. The essential electrical quantities are voltage rating and current-handling capacity. Larger versions of microswitches, fitted in waterproof housings with rollers, etc., are usually referred to as limit switches.

Reed Switches

Reed switches consist of two or more contacts mounted in a glass tube and operated by a magnetic field. Reed switches do not normally contain magnets, but they operate when there is sufficient magnetic flux density lengthwise along the switch. The reed-switch/permanent-magnet combination can be used to sense various mechanical movements as shown in Fig. 7.2. Another way of using reed switches is to employ a fixed magnet to hold the switch normally operated. Release is then effected either by interposing a ferrous-metal vane between the reed and magnet, or by bringing up a more powerful magnet to counteract the first magnet. If an electromagnet is used instead of

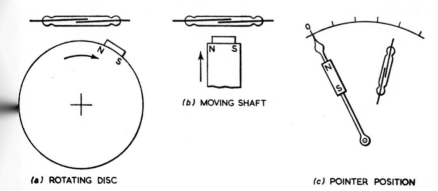

(a) ROTATING DISC   (b) MOVING SHAFT   (c) POINTER POSITION

FIG. 7.2. Use of a reed switch for position sensing.

a permanent magnet it is possible to switch the proximity-sensing action on or off at will. This is useful for selecting one of a number of moving objects, such as machine heads.

Changeover-contact reed switches can also be obtained in which the moving ferrous reed is mechanically biased on to a non-magnetic contact. Application of the magnetic field then moves it over to the magnetic contact. Other changeover switches which may be centre-stable or biased to one side incorporate magnetic bias, either by a magnetized moving reed or by magnetized contacts. These are then polarity-sensitive, moving to one contact or another according to which pole of the operating magnet is brought near.

Reed switches are either evacuated or filled with an inert gas. The gas may be nitrogen, hydrogen or a mixture thereof with other gases, the choice depending on the metals chosen for the contacts. These may be diffused-gold, gold-plated, rhodium-plated, silver alloy, tungsten or mercury-wetted, each having a slight advantage for a particular purpose. In most applications the choice is not critical.

Most reed switches have a characteristic bounce which may last up to a millisecond. Such a duration is insignificant for working into low-speed switching circuits but trouble may be experienced with high-speed logic circuits, which may register two or three counts per operation. Mercury-wetted contacts provide a solution to this problem although they must be operated within a few degrees of angle of a specified plane.

The electrical load of a reed switch must be within the manufacturer's limits if a good life is to be obtained. Provided that this is the case, lifetimes of the order of at least 10^8 operations can be expected. In equipments where reed switches are operated occasionally, say once per minute, 10^8 operations gives a life of 200 years. But if, for example, a reed switch were employed in a pulsing flowmeter in constant use operating 20 times per second, 10^8 operations would give a service life of only 2 months!

Precision Proximity Switch

The reed switch itself is not capable of great precision as its operating point is not well defined and the magnetic field of the operating magnet is likely to be distorted by nearby ferrous objects. A magnetic switch incorporating some of the features of the reed relay, but with high precision of operating point, is manufactured by the Tann Controls Company: see Fig. 7.3. In this switch a pivoted contact blade is held in 'normally-closed' contact by a magnet against the force of a spring. When a piece of ferrous material comes within 0·03 in. of the sensing head, the magnetic force is short-circuited and the spring moves the contact blade to open the circuit.

Acting as it does over such a small distance, this switch is not intended for the more general engineering applications where greater sensitivity is required. It is more suitable for the accurate positioning of parts of machinery such as automatic machine tools.

The life of this switch, of the order of $2–5 \times 10^7$ operations, is almost as great as that of a reed switch. The switch, being magnetically shielded, is able to operate in the presence of magnetic fields and can be installed in ferrous material.

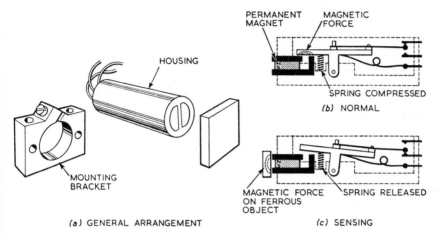

FIG. 7.3. Precision proximity switch. (*Tann Controls Company*)

Capacitive Proximity Switches

Variation of electrical capacitance can be used as a means of proximity sensing in which either the movement of an object itself alters a capacitor field, or the object is linked to one of the capacitor plates to vary its position. The pros and cons of capacitance methods are discussed in Chapter 5. Some capacitive sensing circuits, such as the Miller-Pierce, are fundamentally on/off in their operation and can only function as proximity switches. Most of the other circuits are proportional in their action, giving an output signal which is an analogue of position. These can then be used as proximity switches by the use of an electrical trigger. The liquid-detector probe also described in Chapter 5 is an example, in which a three-terminal capacitance meter incorporates a relay to signal whether or not a pipeline is full of liquid.

Inductive Proximity Sensors

The simple coil sensor used for flowmeter pick-offs, etc. is not strictly a proximity sensor as it responds to velocity rather than position. However, it is a proximity sensor in effect, because the pulsing output signals the number of times the internal magnet has moved past the probe. A number of true inductive proximity sensors are described in Chapter 6. These involve the alteration of either the self or the mutual inductance of coils by the approach of a piece of ferrous material, or the saturation of an inductor core by the approach of a permanent magnet. As with capacitive circuits some of these are fundamentally on/off, while others have analogue outputs looked at with some form of level discriminator.

Optical Proximity Sensors and Counting Systems

The light-beam/photocell combination has long been used for counting boxes on conveyor belts, counting people on escalators, for machinery safety interlocks and similar duties. The various types of photocells are summarized later in this chapter and described in their appropriate sections earlier in this book. Optical sensing is most suited to clean dry areas; some difficulty may be experienced if dirt or moisture is prevalent, as obstruction of the light may cause consequent maloperation.

When counting boxes on a conveyor belt the detector is usually mounted at a hump in the belt, as in Fig. 7.4, to separate momentarily the tops of the boxes. A disadvantage of the optical method for counting is the limited lamp

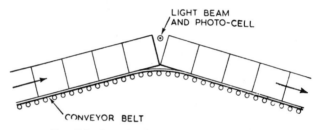

FIG. 7.4. Counting boxes on a conveyor belt.

life and the effect of ambient light. The former can be mitigated by under-running a filament lamp, and both can be overcome by using an a.c. gas-discharge tube as the light source. With a discharge tube the light follows the alternating current in its intensity and the resulting photocell a.c. output component can be amplified, the d.c. level due to ambient light being filtered out.

Another disadvantage of optical sensing (perhaps, indeed, of most sensing devices) applied to counting is the ease with which the output may be modified by an unscrupulous operator. He may decrease the count merely by holding his hand in front of the light while several boxes pass, and increase it by waving his hand several times through the beam. Placing the sensor out of reach of the operative may be a solution, but this is not always possible and may make maintenance difficult.

When the count is particularly important it is necessary to use three sensors so that if one develops a fault it can be seen to differ from the other two. Two counters are not sufficient as if they differ it would not be known which was correct. It might be argued that the higher was correct as such sensors are more likely to lose counts rather than generate spurious ones. However, if some effect had caused the lower counter to lose counts it might also have affected the higher to a lesser extent. The three-count system overcomes this difficulty. In some systems where the reliability must be of a very high order the three sensors are coupled together. (See 'Triplication for Extreme Reliability' later in this chapter.)

A widely-used application of optical proximity sensors is in the automatic registration control of wrapping machines. If a wrapper from a domestic product (such as margarine or soap) is examined, a small dark or coloured rectangle will be seen, usually a short distance from the point where the wrap has been cut from the roll. In the wrapping machine a lamp and photocell unit is focused on to the continuously-moving web of paper or foil, giving out a signal when the registration mark is observed. This triggers the shear to cut the pre-printed wrapper from the roll. In a design by Electronic Switchgear (London) Ltd. a half-silvered mirror is incorporated in the lamp and photocell unit so that the same lens arrangement can be used for focusing the light and photocell on to the wrapper material. This has led to a compact and rugged design.

Ultrasonic Proximity Sensing

Ultrasonic proximity sensing is similar to optical sensing in that it requires a transmitter and receiver with either a direct or reflected path between them. Magnetostrictive sensors are described in Chapter 6, and piezoelectric sensors in Chapter 2. Two systems are in common use. In one, the transmitter is energized continuously, the output from the receiver decreasing when the path is obscured; in the other, the transmitter and receiver are connected to the output and input respectively of a high-gain amplifier. When the path between them is unobscured a feedback oscillation rapidly builds up, analogous to the 'howl' of public-address systems when the microphones and loudspeakers are incorrectly placed. The system is then either oscillating or not oscillating according to whether the path is unobscured or obscured.

The ultrasonic transmitters and receivers are not usually affected by dirt or moisture and can be hidden if necessary. As the operating frequency is above the audible range the system is not likely to be detected or cause annoyance, except perhaps to animals.

Radioactive Tracers

If a particle of radioactive material is fixed to an object, then the approach of the object can be detected with a radiation detector. Owing to the potential hazards of radioactive material in unskilled hands such methods do not find wide application. There are, however, particular cases where the method is invaluable. When solid objects or 'go-devils' are sent down liquid or gas pipelines and become jammed against sediment or foreign bodies they can be located externally if they contain a small radioactive source. The method has also been used by ecologists to study the movement underground of moles and other small animals. With a sensitive Geiger counter the source can be very small and cause no harm to the animal.

Triplication for Extreme Reliability

Although electronic sensing devices can now be made to a high order of reliability, occasions do arise when ultimate reliability is required. Such a requirement occurs in nuclear reactor control, in the processing of expensive materials, in accounting systems, and wherever danger to human life is involved. There is little advantage to be gained from using two sensing devices instead of one, as in the event of failure there remains an ambiguity. The usual practice is therefore to use three sensing devices so that when any one fails it can be identified as the 'odd man out'. This *redundancy technique* is often incorporated in on-line computer control systems using analogue and on/off sensors. The principle is easier to apply to on/off systems such as proximity sensors and counters; a typical logic circuit using NOR blocks is shown in Fig. 7.5.

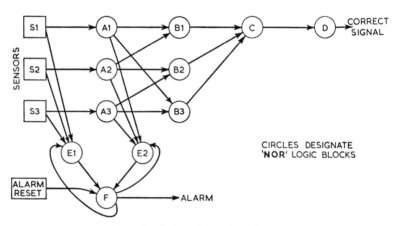

FIG. 7.5. Logic for triplication of sensors.

When the sensors operate, their outputs change from 0 to 1 and an opposite or inverted signal appears at the outputs of blocks A1, A2 and A3. Blocks B1, B2 and B3 detect when any two A-blocks are at 0, thus detecting when any two of the sensors have operated. The three possibilities are collected together by block C resulting in another inversion which is corrected by block D. The output from block D thus agrees with the majority of the inputs ignoring any one which differs.

Under normal conditions all the sensors give out 0 or all give out 1. Under fault conditions there is a mixture of 0's and 1's which are detected as 1's both before and after inversion by blocks A1, A2 and A3. This error detection i performed by blocks E1 and E2, the outputs of which both become 0 under fault conditions. The two 0's are detected by block F which feeds the resulting 1 back into blocks E1 and E2 to hold on or remember the fault indication. This is then released by feeding a 1 signal into F by the alarm reset as shown. An obvious shortcoming of the arrangement in the event of a fault is the inability to register which sensor caused the maloperation; but the facility can easily be provided at the expense of a few more logic blocks if required. It is usually necessary to incorporate a delay in the alarm circuit to prevent spurious alarms being generated by slight timing differences between the pulses from different sensors.

DIMENSION SENSORS

Dimension sensors answer questions such as: 'How much is a certain distance, how thick is a certain object or how large is a certain angle?' They may be required to measure very small displacements, as do the error detectors in servo and force-balance systems. In these cases linearity is not very important, but in most cases where an analogue of dimension is required the linearity is of great concern. As mentioned in connection with proximity sensors, most physical quantities can be converted into a displacement as an initial stage in obtaining an analogue signal of the quantity. Examples are given later in this chapter. Digital position-sensors provide the best that can be achieved in accuracy and repeatability and present the signal in the form most often required by computers.

Variable-resistor Transmitters

A distinction is drawn between variable resistors, which give a current signal, and potentiometers, which give a voltage signal, although there is no real difference in the sensing device itself. Variable-resistor systems are characterized by low accuracy and simple readout or indicating devices. Automobile electrical systems are typical of this; for example, petrol level is frequently signalled by the movement of a float coupled to a variable resistor. Errors of less than 5 per cent are seldom required in such cases.

With a linear variable resistor the resistance is proportional to the movement of the wiper arm. The current in a simple circuit (and thus also the meter deflection) then follows a non-linear law. If it is not acceptable to calibrate the meter accordingly, the non-linearity is corrected by winding the resistor on a shaped former to give the appropriate correction.

Potentiometer Transmitters

The term potentiometer, originally by definition a device for measuring potential, has now come to apply to any resistor which has a third terminal connected to a wiper that can make contact at a variable point along the

resistor. Potentiometers, usually rotary or rectilinear in form, can be manu
factured to almost any degree of precision. Rotary potentiometers may be o
the single-turn type, with or without end-stops, and the winding may occup
up to almost the entire 360 degrees of rotation. A variation of the rotar
pattern is the helical potentiometer in which the shaft is free to rotate for u
to twenty turns while the slider moves along a resistance helix. Precisio
servo potentiometers are usually manufactured to conform to the inter
national standard servo mounting in one of a number of standard fram
sizes.

The basic variables associated with potentiometers are resistance, linearity
power-rating, resolution, starting torque or force, and mechanical travel
The linearity of the best servo potentiometers is of the order of ± 0.1 per cent
The resolution depends on the pitch of the resistance wire used: it may b
'infinite' in the case of metal film potentiometers. Infinite resolution may als
be obtained using resistance wire in a helical potentiometer where the heli:
consists of plain (unwound) resistance wire.

An application of potentiometers is in load transducers where the deflection
of an elastic member under the stress of an applied force is magnified t
operate a wiper arm. By careful design an accuracy of ± 1 per cent can b
achieved, but the limiting factor to further accuracy is the friction of th
wiper arm and of the pivots or bearings of the lever system used to magnif
the deflection.

The wipers of potentiometers, being the most critical part, have been th
subject of some research. Precious metals of various types are used to achiev
reliable contact with minimal contact force.

A potentiometer generates an electrical potential or, more precisely, a rati
of potentials. If the electrical output is to follow the mechanical input it mus
be measured on a high-impedance instrument. The choice will depend on th
application and availability, but it may fall on a digital voltmeter, electroni
feedback voltmeter or another potentiometer in a feedback servo system.

Strain Gauges

Strain gauges made from metals, semiconductors and piezoelectric material
are described in Chapter 2. They are used for measuring the small strain
experienced in structures, bridges, aircraft, etc. When the strain is of a periodi
nature as induced by vibration a piezoelectric strain gauge is preferred. Fo
more elastic structures made of plastics or rubber the Dracone electrolyti
strain gauge described in Chapter 3 can be used. Many of the more sensitiv
of the capacitive and inductive dimension-sensors can also be pressed int
service for the measurement of strain. Sometimes it is required to measur
the angular deflection from the horizontal of a structure under stress. Th
Electrolevel described in Chapter 3 provides an answer to this problem. Othe
varieties of electrolytic angle transmitters are able to signal a deviation of u
to 40° from the horizontal.

Capacitive Dimension Sensors

Capacitive methods are described in Chapter 5 and the relative merits of two-terminal and three-terminal systems discussed. Capacitive methods are very sensitive—distances down to one microinch can be measured—but care must be taken if accurate results are to be obtained. Capacitive methods are usually limited to the measurement of small distances because large distances represent such small values of capacitance. However, by using a multiple differential capacitor distances of several feet can be measured.

Inductive Dimension Sensors

The various forms of variable inductance and differential transformer described in Chapter 6 provide reliable means of sensing distances, usually small distances. They cannot be said to be particularly convenient as the signal is a.c. and requires a phase-sensitive detector to transform it to a more useful positive and negative d.c. signal. Similarly the Selsyn angular transmitter described is not universally applicable as another similar transmitter is required to transduce the signal into its original form. However, in the remote display of the position of an actuator under manual control, they have found useful application.

Optical Dimension Sensing

Optical methods are sometimes used for sensing small displacements such as occur in force-balance systems used for measuring weight. The very smallest displacements are measured in terms of wavelengths of light by optical interference effects.

Radioactive Thickness Gauges

When a beam of β particles is directed at a material some of the particles are transmitted, some absorbed and some reflected. The proportions of each depend on the dimensions and properties of the material. These effects provide a means of measuring thickness. The simplest arrangement for measuring the thickness of sheet material is to place a radioactive β source on one side and a β-particle detector on the other. Equipments of this type are in common use for a variety of materials, ranging from paper and plastics to metals like steel and brass.

The proportion of the incident beam that is reflected or 'backscattered' can often be used in applications where access to both sides is inconvenient. Portable equipments can be obtained for measuring the wall-thickness of pipes and boilers so that the amount of corrosion can be gauged. When two different materials are in contact (as, for example, a sheet of rubber on a steel roller) a combination of transmission and backscatter can be used. The β particles from a combined source and detector pass through the rubber and are backscattered by the roller, finally passing through the rubber again to be measured by the detector. For measurement of greater thicknesses of metal, γ-ray or X-ray beams are used. A convenient X-ray source uses a phenomenon known as *bremsstrahlung* (braking rays): β particles are slowed down by a foil of suitable material and, in the action of slowing down, radiation is emitted in the direction of the β particles.

Echo Distance Sensing

Both ultrasonic and radio waves are used for measurement of distance by timing the transit of a pulse. A particular application of ultrasonics for level measurement is given later in this chapter.

Digital Position Systems

A simple form of digital transmitter for signalling the position of an object free to move in a straight line would be a row of fixed contacts with a sliding contact on the movable object. The accuracy of position is dependent on the number of fixed contacts and for high accuracy a large number of contacts is required; 100 for 1 per cent accuracy and 1000 for 0·1 per cent. It would be impractical to connect up 1000 or even 100 contacts with individual wires: it is necessary to use a code to simplify matters. Fig. 7.6 shows an example of a decimal code transducer and readout. Connecting the units are ten wires for

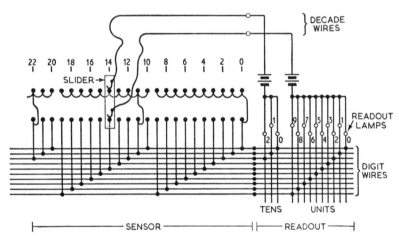

FIG. 7.6. Decimal code system.

the digits and one wire for each decade. Each decade wire is connected to a contact on the slider. If the readout is in numerical form, using indicators such as the edge-lit type, the display would show the number of the station at which the slider was standing. There would be no indication of position while the slider was moving between stations.

A further reduction in the number of wires is achieved if a pure binary code system is adopted as shown in Fig. 7.7. Five binary digits (referred to a 'bits') are needed to transduce the 23 positions but the five-lamp indication is much less easy to read. In order to determine the position of the slider it is necessary to add together the numbers corresponding to the readout lamps illuminated. Now suppose it is necessary for the readout to be in decimal notation and a large number of stations is involved. What are the possibilities of converting from the binary code, ideal for transmission, to the decimal code for display?

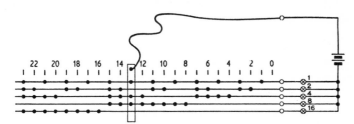

FIG. 7.7. Binary code system.

It is quite easy to convert a number up to ten from decimal to binary and vice versa using a diode matrix such as that shown in Fig. 7.8. Each binary digit '1' is signalled by +10 V and the digit '0' by zero volts. Inverse inputs, the opposite of the original, are obtained from inverter circuits—which may be relays or single transistors. These inverse outputs are designated 1*, 2*, 3* and 4*. Each output wire is biased at +10 V by the resistors R. When a particular binary coded number is inserted at the input, all the outputs except

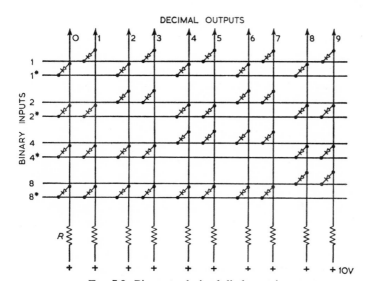

FIG. 7.8. Binary to decimal diode matrix.

the correct one are short-circuited to 0 by one or more of the diodes. Naturally R must be small enough to drive the following circuit but large enough to enable the diode to drag the potential of the wires down to zero. There is a loss of power in the conversion which must be allowed for by subsequent amplification. Although standard practice for numbers up to about 20 or 30, it is prohibitively complicated to perform conversion of large numbers in this way. It is then necessary to perform a sequential conversion by computer methods. For this reason when a display in decimal is required the signals are often conveyed in binary-coded decimal (b.c.d.) form—a very convenient 'cross' between the two codes. In b.c.d. each decimal is transmitted in a four-bit binary code. For example the number 369 would be represented by:

$$0011 \ (\equiv 3); \quad 0110 \ (\equiv 6); \quad 1001 \ (\equiv 9).$$

As with the decimal transducer, both the pure binary and binary-coded decimal transducers operate only when the slider is at a particular station and not in an intermediate position. This is unsuitable for many practical applications where the slider may occupy an indeterminate position which may be anywhere along the track.

The reflected binary code (Gray code) overcomes this difficulty as only one digit changes at a time. The contacts of our model would extend from one station to another, the code change taking place half-way between stations. Even the reflected binary code is not a complete answer because we still have the translation problem if the display is to be in decimal notation. Other codes have been proposed to overcome the difficulties but further discussion is beyond the scope of this book. Table 7.1. compares the binary, b.c.d. and reflected-binary codes with the decimal code.

If, instead of signalling the position of the slider, it were required to drive it to a particular station, similar principles would apply. Many other codes which lead to simplifications in particular situations can be derived. For feeding data into computers it is best to comply with the input coding so that conversion as an initial step within the computer is avoided.

Sometimes the simpler incremental coding system can be employed. Consider our initial model of Fig. 7.6, modified so that all the fixed contacts on one row are connected together and the slider is initially at one end. If the slider moves along the line the wiping contact sends back a series of pulses. If these pulses were fed into a counter then the count registered would correspond to the position of the slider. The main disadvantage in such a simple system is that if the slider changes direction the record is lost.

A system with the mechanical advantages of the incremental method but without the risk of losing the signal were power momentarily cut off, is the Perkin-Elmer One-Brush encoder. This consists of a number of commutator bars of printed-circuit construction over which a single brush moves. A series of 18 output busbars (for a 1000-count unit) are also incorporated in the

Table 7.1. Comparison of Digital Codes

Decimal	Binary	Binary-coded Decimal	Reflected Binary
0	0	0000 0000	0
1	1	0000 0001	1
2	10	0000 0010	11
3	11	0000 0011	10
4	100	0000 0100	110
5	101	0000 0101	111
6	110	0000 0110	101
7	111	0000 0111	100
8	1000	0000 1000	1100
9	1001	0000 1001	1101
10	1010	0001 0000	1111
11	1011	0001 0001	1110
12	1100	0001 0010	1010
13	1101	0001 0011	1011
14	1110	0001 0100	1001
15	1111	0001 0101	1000
16	10000	0001 0110	11000
17	10001	0001 0111	11001
18	10010	0001 1000	11011
19	10011	0001 1001	11010
20	10100	0010 0000	11110
21	10101	0010 0001	11111
22	10110	0010 0010	11101
23	10111	0010 0011	11100
24	11000	0010 0100	10100
25	11001	0010 0101	10101

printed assembly and each of the commutator bars is connected to one of the output busbars, as shown in Fig. 7.9. The brush is also connected to the read-out either by means of a flexible connector for limited rotation or a slip-ring for continuous rotation. The commutator bars are connected via a signal-steering circuit into a digital register. As the brush moves over the commutator bars a non-repetitive sequence is generated which sets the registers to correspond with shaft position. After switching on, or after a momentary power failure, the signal stored in the register has no meaning; however, it is only necessary for the brush to move over a short distance for the register to become correctly set.

The commutator bars can be very narrow, so that as many as 100 can be accommodated in 1 in. of track. The width of the brush is small compared with the radial length of the commutator bars so the brush may be re-positioned from time to time thus increasing the life of the assembly. As only one brush is used the assembly has low inertia and friction.

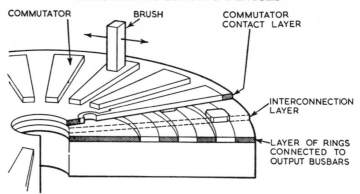

FIG. 7.9. One-brush encoder. (*Perkin-Elmer*)

Both rotary and rectilinear transducers can be obtained. The output of the register is in a minimum-switching code, not of itself particularly useful, but standard associated equipment is used to convert this to a standard code.

MOTION

In this section we are concerned with the measurement of velocity or speed. The commonest speed indicator, the automobile drag-cup speedometer, can hardly be classed as an electronic sensing device although it operates on the principle of electromagnetic induction. The circuit, consisting merely of a disc of aluminium in the 'drag' of a rotating magnet, is certainly one of the most elementary of electric circuits.

Velocity sensors are frequently required in servo systems in conjunction with position sensors to facilitate control. Electric generators designed to have a linear voltage/speed relationship for this purpose are known as tacho-generators. Where the rotation of a shaft or turbine is signalled by means of a pulsed pick-off sensor the resulting pulse train can be converted to give a value for velocity by the circuit of Fig. 7.16.

Besides velocity (dx/dt), two other quantities can be classed as motion. They are acceleration (d^2x/dt^2) and 'jerk' (d^3x/dt^3). Accelerometers are now fairly commonplace, ranging from the simple piezoelectric and inductive devices described in Chapters 2 and 6 to the highly sophisticated accelero-meters used in inertial navigation systems which are outside the scope of this book. Jerk, the rate of change of acceleration, can be obtained by differen-tiating the output from an accelerometer, although devices have been made for sensing it directly. Jerk has physiological importance because it is jerk rather than acceleration that causes injury to persons falling on to a hard surface. If an acceleration is applied slowly as in a centifuge chamber it is possible for muscles and tissues to distribute themselves to withstand the forces applied. With jerk this is not possible and injury may result.

WEIGHT AND FORCE

The electrical measurement of weight is not difficult in itself, except that higher accuracy is often needed with weight measurements than with the measurement of plant parameters such as temperature, pressure, etc. High precision is usually necessary to satisfy Government regulations designed to prevent goods being sold underweight. If inaccurate weighing equipment is used it is necessary to have a large 'give away' in order to ensure that goods are never sold below the stated weight. Electronic weighing devices are of two main types, load cells and force-balance weigh heads.

Load Cells

A load cell consists of a structure which deflects when a load is applied to it, together with a mechanism for measuring and transmitting the deflection. The deflection is commonly measured by strain gauges, as in the example in Chapter 2. There is little difficulty with these devices in reaching an accuracy of ± 1 per cent or even ± 0.2 per cent, but when an accuracy better than ± 0.1 per cent is required then the shortcomings start to be apparent. The two major errors are non-linearity and long-term drift. Strain gauges using metal wires are, on the whole, limited to relatively heavy-duty applications. Semiconductor strain gauges on the other hand are opening up the field for the measurement of loads of the order of grams or ounces because of their much greater sensitivity.

An instrument for measuring forces in general (rather than only weight, which is a particular kind of force) is known as a dynamometer. In most applications dynamometers and load-cells are equivalent. An example of a dynamometer, shown in Fig. 7.10, consists of a precisely machined metal ring (known as a proving ring) with an l.v.d.t. to measure the deflection under

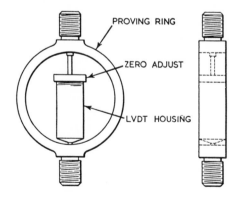

Fig. 7.10. Dynamometer using an l.v.d.t. (*Schaevitz Engineering type TDC-4*)

applied forces. The operation of l.v.d.t's is described in Chapter 6. A load cell which makes use of the variation of magnetic permeability of a material with strain is the Pressductor load-cell also described in Chapter 6.

A simple load switch can be made from the combination of a deflecting member, such as a proving ring, and a microswitch. Such devices are commercially available with an adjustment on the microswitch enabling the device to be set for a particular weight or force.

It is also possible to obtain load transmitters in which the deflection of an elastic member is magnified by a mechanical lever to drive the wiper arm of a potentiometer. The success of these devices in achieving an accuracy of ± 1 per cent is a tribute to their manufacturers, but the method cannot be regarded as a good one.

Force-balance Weighing Systems

This is a method used for high-speed weighing in which the applied load is counterbalanced by a force applied by an electromagnetic coil. As it is possible to manufacture a coil and magnet assembly with a good long-term stability of current/load relationship, the method provides an accurate weighing system. The essential features (apart from the obvious mechanical supports) are a deflection sensor, an amplifier and the force coil. Fig. 7.11 shows the action of a force-balance system. In (i) there is no weight on the scale pan which is kept in position with a light spring. In (ii) a weight is placed on the scale pan and the spring deflects until limited by a mechanical end-stop. If now, as in (iii), a force-balance coil is brought into action the scale pan is restored nearly to its original position. The current in the balance coil is now an analogue of the applied force, the slight deflection from the original position being of no consequence. If it is required to balance com-

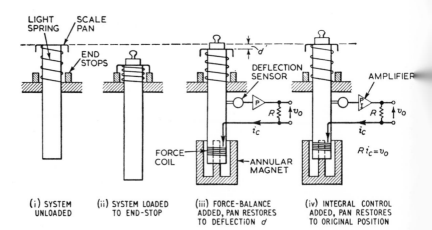

FIG. 7.11. Illustration of force-balance system.

ɔletely with no deflection an integral action is required in the amplifier. The ɛrror is then reduced to that of the threshold level of the amplifier.

If the weight is put on and off, the system will oscillate for a few cycles ɛach time until balance is obtained. In systems where the fastest response is ʳequired a velocity coil, adjacent to the balance coil, is incorporated to give ɩn output proportional to velocity and is connected to the amplifier to obtain ɩ balance condition in the shortest possible time. However, without a ᴠelocity coil balance can be obtained in less than 100 ms. In the simple system ᴡithout error-integral feedback the slight deflection in the balanced condition ᴤ essential as it provides the input to the amplifier. Thus the error signal ᴍultiplied by amplifier gain is equal to balance-coil current. The 'stiffness' ɔf the system is proportional to overall gain.

An alternative to the analogue balancing system described above is the ᴅigital method. In this method a number of standard currents corresponding ᴏ weights of, say, 1, 2, 4, 8 oz . . . are available and can be switched into the ᴄoil by means of high-speed solid-state switches. A logic unit switches the ᴤtandard currents on and off in a manner similar to the balancing of a ᴅigital voltmeter until balance is obtained. The digital method is an accurate ᴏne but costly, and is not likely to be used unless a digital signal is required ɓy a computer. If speed is not important it is possible to construct a digital ɓalancing system using mechanical switches which is very accurate ɩndeed.

Three methods of sensing the deflection error of force-balance weighing ᴤystems are in common use, capacitive, optical and differential-transformer. ᴛhe capacitive method, in which the centre earthed electrode of a differential ᴄapacitor is attached to the moving assembly, is extremely sensitive but ʳequires a dry atmosphere for reliable operation. The optical method which ɩnvolves a lamp, a photocell and a mask which moves between them is ʳobust and as reliable as the lamp. With the differential transformer, a means ɔf converting the a.c. signal to d.c. has generally to be provided as well as a ᴤuitable electrical supply.

In a purely force-balance system (as in the examples given above) any ᴠibration in the mounting support is likely to be seen in an amplified form ɩn the output signal. A considerable reduction of vibration sensitivity is ᴀchieved in the Telomex force balance head intended primarily for check-ᴡeighing operations where most of the weight of the load is counterbalanced. ᴛhe balance coil then only supplies the difference between the counterweight ᴀnd the weight of the load. As vibration acts on the counterweight as well as ᴛhe load its effect is greatly reduced.

Weigh-heads of this type are not very easy to waterproof. It is not possible ᴛo seal the weighing shaft except by means of a labyrinth seal in which inter-ᴍeshing cups increase the distance from outside to inside. In critical applica-ᴛions a slight air purge from inside to outside can be applied to prevent ɩngress of moisture.

Sensing of Specific Gravity

The simplest way of sensing and transmitting the specific gravity of a liquid in a tank is perhaps by having a weight suspended in the liquid from a load cell. Variations in the specific gravity will be signalled as variations in the immersed weight. For applications where the specific gravity of a liquid running through a pipe has to be measured the Sperry Gravitymaster provides a means. The instrument consists of a U-shaped length of pipe connected by two bellows. The weight of the U section represents the specific gravity of the liquid filling it. A force-balance system is used for sensing the weight.

PRESSURE

High-vacuum Gauges

The Pirani gauge described in Chapter 2 makes use of the variation of thermal conductivity of a gas with pressure. Apart from this device, which measures the cooling effect of the gas on hot resistance thermometers, the majority of electronic vacuum gauges employ the currents produced by gaseous ions, the province of Chapter 4. The McLeod gauge remains as the standard reference instrument against which other gauges are calibrated.

Pressure and Low-vacuum Gauges

Electronic pressure gauges involve a diaphragm, a spring and some means of detecting displacement. Low-vacuum gauges have been included in this section as low vacua are amenable to measurement by the diaphragm/spring displacement technique. Pressure gauges are available either as differential gauge or absolute pressure sensors. In differential pressure sensors, access to both sides of the diaphragm is possible and the device does not respond to standing pressure on both sides. Differential pressure sensors are used for measuring air velocity with Pitot tubes and liquid level by hydrostatic pressure also for measuring the density of a liquid by measuring the difference of hydrostatic pressure at two different levels. In gauge-pressure sensors one side of the diaphragm is connected to atmosphere and in absolute-pressure sensors one side is evacuated.

Fig. 7.12 shows a pressure sensor manufactured by the Consolidated Electrodynamics Division, Bell and Howell Ltd. The pressure to be measured causes displacement of the diaphragm and a cross-shaped spring to which it is connected by the force rod. Posts of insulating material (sapphire) are fixed to the spring. Resistance wire, wound on the sapphire posts as shown, is initially in tension on both sides. Application of the force increases the tension on one side while decreasing it on the other and so an output is obtained. This technique is applicable to the measurement of pressures from 1 lbf/in upwards.

As with many instruments the development of pressure transducers has been spurred on by the requirements of military and aero-space programmes

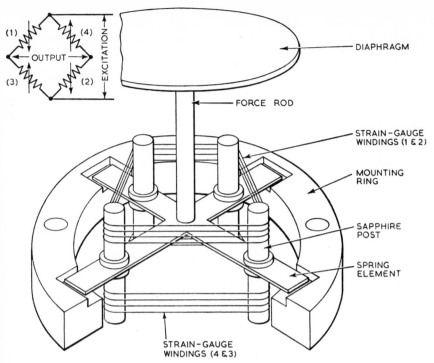

FIG. 7.12. Strain gauge, pressure sensor. (*Consolidated Electrodynamics Division, Bell & Howell Ltd.*)

and as a consequence many other strain-gauge or differential-transformer pressure transducers are now commercially available. The most sensitive diaphragm pressure gauges are those employing capacitive sensing of displacement. An example of one of these, the Decker instrument, is given in Chapter 5.

The force-balance technique where the force on a diaphragm is balanced by the force from an electromagnet coil is used for process pressure transmitting where the signal is required in one of the standard forms, such as 0–20 mA or 4–20 mA.

LEVEL

Level Detectors

When a vessel has to be maintained with liquid to a given level and where float valves will not suffice, then either conductivity level detectors or floats operating proximity switches may be used.

The electrolytic conductivity probe has been in use for some years and has given reliable service using thermionic valves in the associated electronic units: even more reliable service can be expected using transistors. The device is extremely simple. It consists of a rigid rod mounted on an insulating support and extending down to the level to be detected. The rod is connected to an electronic unit which supplies a small a.c. potential to the rod and senses when this is short-circuited by the rising liquid. The electronic unit usually contains a relay to switch on motors, alarms, etc.

Two modes of operation are allowed for to enable the correct 'fail safe' conditions to be obtained. In one mode the relay is normally operated and is released by the rising liquid touching the probe. In the other mode the relay is normally released and is operated by the rising liquid. The question of which mode is to be used poses the question: What is a safe condition? In some plants a safe condition would be to switch off all pumps to prevent any liquid overflowing on to the floor, the condition of an empty tank not being a serious matter. In other plants, e.g. where cooling liquid was being stored, it might be safer to keep the tank full at all times, even at the risk of overflow under fault conditions. Fig. 7.13 shows how one control unit can be used with two probes to control both high and low level on a vessel. Contact A1 isolates the low-level probe while the liquid rises towards the upper level.

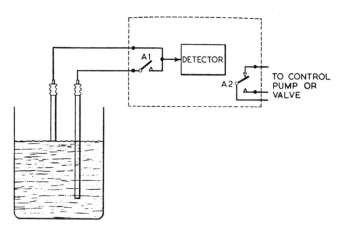

FIG. 7.13. High and low level control.

Conductivity level-detectors cannot of course be used with insulating liquids; nevertheless a high-sensitivity unit will operate on liquids having a resistivity as much as 200 MΩ-cm.

When it is necessary to measure liquid level in closed vessels where conductivity probes are not convenient, a radioactive method can be used. This involves a β-ray emitter (such as cobalt 60) mounted in a shielded housing on one side of the tank, and a detector on the other. When the liquid rises past the β-ray beam the radiation is absorbed and the level is signalled. Devices of this type are able to 'see' through the metal walls of vessels without any apertures having to be cut.

Level Transmitters

A common problem in industry is the measurement and transmission of the level of liquids in tanks and powder or granules in hoppers and silos. With a conducting liquid a variable capacitor method such as the Fielden Telstor, described in Chapter 5, is applicable. Where the density of a liquid is known and is constant throughout the mass, the level can be gauged by measuring the hydrostatic pressure at the bottom of the vessel. Differential pressure cells are used for this purpose with the reference input at atmospheric pressure (or that at the surface of the liquid if this is not atmospheric). Some instruments operate by weighing a cylindrical displacer immersed in the liquid. As the level rises the apparent weight of the displacer decreases.

Another approach, well suited to very large tanks and silos, is the Endress and Hauser Silopilot with electronic servo. In this instrument a cylinder containing a transformer and capacitor plates is suspended from a pulley arrangement over the liquid. A detector and servo system keeps the cylinder at a fixed distance above the liquid surface by proximity measurement. The position of the float is thus an indication of liquid level. As the cylinder never touches the liquid it is kept clean and free from corrosion. In a similar arrangement with a mechanical servo, used for solids, the 'float' touches the surface of the material.

Level can also be measured by timing a pulsed ultrasonic beam reflected from the surface of the liquid. In some equipments one ultrasonic transducer serves for both transmission and reception while others employ separate transducers. They may be either mounted at the top of the tank to operate through air, or fixed underneath the bottom of the tank and operate through the liquid, obtaining in both cases a reflection from the surface of the liquid. When using ultrasonic methods care must be taken that other effects do not contribute excessive error. For example, the velocity of sound in air is affected by variations of temperature, pressure and humidity.

In some cases it becomes impossible to measure level and the tank has to be weighed by incorporating one or more load cells in the mounting structure. For really large tanks this can be difficult, and care must be taken that rigid pipe connections do not contribute error. With the extremely sensitive load cells now available error due to movement of pipes, etc., can be kept small as the deflection of the cell under full load can be as small as 0·001 in.

FLOW

There are two fundamentally different kinds of flowmeter, namely, inferential and positive-displacement. In inferential meters, movement of the liquid imparts a movement, tension or displacement to some physical member by virtue of the movement of the liquid. As the liquid velocity approaches zero the effect disappears. In positive-displacement meters the liquid forces pistons through defined paths sweeping a definite volume. As the liquid velocity reduces there is ideally no difference in the effect on the piston. In practice leakage past the piston occurs which becomes significant at low flow-rates.

The only truly electronic instrument is the magnetic flowmeter described in Chapter 6, although there are a number of ways in which electronics contributes improvements to more conventional flowmeters.

The turbine flowmeter illustrated in Fig. 7.14 has the desirable property of being hydrodynamically balanced so that the rotor rotates without axial thrust on the bearings. The forward thrust of the liquid on the rotor blades is counteracted by a reverse thrust on a cone-shaped section of the rotor. Rotation of the turbine is detected by means of a magnet embedded in the

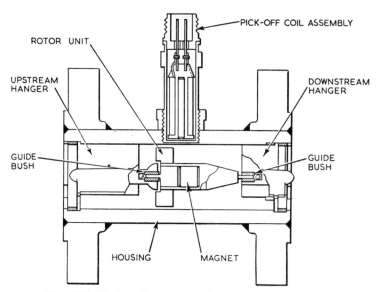

FIG. 7.14. Turbine flowmeter. (*Gloster Equipment Limited*)

rotor and a pick-off sensor on the outside of the flowmeter chamber. As the turbine rotates rapidly a simple coil pick-off is satisfactory. If situations arise with flowmeters where the moving part moves slowly then a magnetometer probe can be used. Descriptions of both methods are given in Chapter 6. Although not classed as a positive-displacement meter, turbine rotor blades are almost frictionless and slice their way through the flowing liquid measuring out definite volumes.

Most flowmeters, even positive-displacement types, vary slightly in their pulse rate per gallon under changes of liquid viscosity, temperature, density etc. In some types of flowmeter having an accessible output shaft, a gearbox is incorporated between the meter and recording mechanism or pulsing micro-switch. When using an electronic pick-off it is, of course, not possible to use a mechanical gearbox, but there is an 'electronic gearbox' (described below) in which pulse rates can be converted by predetermined ratios. By this means a flowmeter may be set up in the user's factory under its normal operating conditions and the 'electronic gearbox' ratio adjusted until the system gives out the required number of pulses per gallon.

The cooling effect on a hot wire provides a means of measuring the flow-rate of gases. The 'hot wire anemometer' works on this principle. A brief description of the techniques employed is given in Chapter 2.

When a magnetic flowmeter and a particle-concentration meter (such as the Mawdsley 'Emsol' described in Chapter 3) are combined and their output signals multiplied together, the result is the total volume of particulate material that has passed. This can occasionally be of use in quarrying or handling metal ores, etc.

Handling of Flowmeter Pulses

A frequent requirement of pulsing flowmeter systems is the production of a train of uniform pulses, each of which represents a definite volume of liquid. The flowmeter system can then be described, e.g. as giving an output of so many pulses per gallon. When the flowmeter gives more pulses per gallon than is convenient the pulse-rate may be reduced by the 'electronic gearbox' shown in Fig. 7.15. After shaping, the pulses are fed into a binary

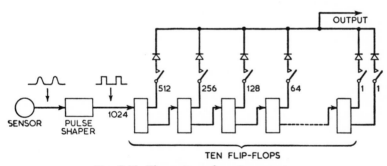

FIG. 7.15. Flowmeter pulse rate converter.

counter made up of a number of flip-flops. Each stage divides the pulses by two. The diagram indicates ten flip-flops, i.e. division by $2^{10} = 1024$. By closing appropriate switches any number of output pulses from 1 to 1024 can be obtained from 1024 input pulses. Thus the switch settings for a particular application determine the ratio of output pulses to flowmeter pulses.

Another common requirement is a voltage signal proportional to flow-rate.

Fig. 7.16 shows one way of achieving it. The pulses from the pulse shaper are of constant width and amplitude so the required signal is represented by the average voltage of the pulses. A simple method of averaging uses an operational amplifier as shown. If the pulse frequency is f, then the time-separation between the front edges of successive pulses is $1/f$. The average input voltage

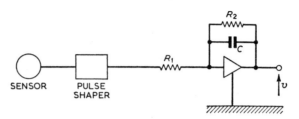

FIG. 7.16. Pulse rate to voltage converter.

is Vt_wf for a pulse width (duration) of t_w. As the current into the amplifier is virtually zero, then

$$v/R_2 = Vt_wf/R_1, \quad \text{that is,} \quad v \propto f.$$

The capacitor is required to provide an averaging effect by storing energy between pulses. The output voltage v is thus proportional to the flowmeter pick-off frequency.

Mass Flowmeters

With both liquids and solids it is frequently required to know the total mass that has passed a certain point rather than the volume. For liquids a combination of volume flowmeter and density measuring device would provide the answer, except that it is not easy to measure the density of liquids flowing in a pipeline. Various ingenious mass flowmeters have been put forward and operate quite satisfactorily. One method uses a rotary paddle to impart movement to the liquid and a second paddle to recover all the energy of rotation. This produces a deflection proportional to mass flow.

The example given here, in Fig. 7.17, is the Decker true-mass flowmeter. It has a loop of pipework through which the liquid is made to flow. The loop of pipe has gyroscopic properties due to the flowing liquid; more precisely the gyroscopic properties are proportional to mass flow-rate. The loop of pipe is coupled to the inlet and outlet pipes with high-quality rubber tubing. The device depends on the well known property of gyroscopes that when a torque is applied along one axis in the plane of the gyroscope, then the gyroscope rotates with a 'precessional velocity' about a third axis orthogonal to the other two. In the Decker instrument a constant torque is not applied, but the loop is vibrated through a small angle at constant amplitude, so developing an alternating gyro-coupling torque about the mutually orthogonal axis the peak amplitude of which is proportional to mass flow-rate. The torque acts against an elastic restraint (torque bars) to produce an alternating displacement about the torque axis. This displacement is then sensed by vibration transducers and the resulting peak amplitude signal is directly proportional to mass flowrate. When converted to d.c. the mass flow-rate signal can be integrated to provide the total mass that has flowed in any given period.

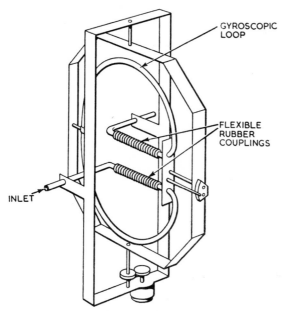

FIG. 7.17. Gyro mass flowmeter. (*The Decker Corporation*)

OPTICAL SENSING

References to photoelectric sensors and optical methods, made elsewhere in this book, are summarized here. Photoconductive cells, photodiodes, photo-transistors and photovoltaic cells are described in Chapter 2. Photoemissive cells, both vacuum and gas-filled, are described in Chapter 4 together with electron multipliers and image intensifiers. A brief mention of the photo-magnetic effect is given in Chapter 6. The use of photoelectric devices for proximity detection and machine registration is described in Chapter 7, while infra-red absorption is described in Chapter 8.

Apart from the photoelectric effects already described in the above sections here are one or two other semiconductor sensors which offer advantages in particular situations. They are extensions of the effect whereby hole-electron pairs are released in semiconductors by the action of light. One of these is the photothyristor sold under various trade names. A normal thyristor consists of four alternate layers of p-type and n-type material, normally non-conducting, but which conducts on the application of a momentary trigger signal. In the photothyristor the trigger signal is a momentary light flash. If alternating voltage is applied to photo-thyristors, then in common with ordinary thyristors they are 'turned off' every half cycle. Under a.c. conditions it is therefore necessary to have a continuous illumination if the device is to remain turned on for the maximum possible time in each cycle.

The performance of photocell systems is often impaired by the 'dark' current which flows and which increases with temperature. The effect can often be overcome by interposing a rotating shutter between the lamp and photocell and using an a.c. coupled amplifier. Only the part of the photocell signal of interest is then amplified. A similar effect can sometimes be obtained using an a.c. amplifier and working from the 'ripple' of an a.c. excited filament or gas-discharge lamp.

Instruments are commercially available for measuring the colour of process liquids. Some of these using a single beam of light have to be periodically calibrated due to change of lamp output. They respond also to turbidity in the liquid. The arrangement of Fig. 7.18 enables colour to be measured apart from turbidity. Light from the lamp can take two paths through the

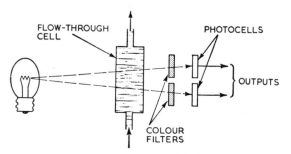

FIG. 7.18. Schematic arrangement for dye colour measurement.

sample cell or 'cuvette'. Each path has a colour filter, one designed to ignore the process-liquid colour and the other to be attenuated by it. For example, when measuring the intensity of a yellow dye the filters may be red and green. The red light is not affected by the yellow dye whereas the green light is attenuated. The outputs from the two photocells must then be ratioed by a suitable dividing circuit. If selenium cells are used feeding into a high-resistance load the outputs are proportional to the logarithm of the light intensity. A very simple form of dividing circuit, Fig. 7.19, operates by subtracting the outputs of the two photocells. If the normal light intensity with clear liquid is I and if the attenuation due to colour and turbidity is α and τ respectively then the output of the cell in the red beam will be proportional to log $(I\tau$

and that in the green beam will be proportional log ($I\alpha\tau$). Subtraction of the red-cell output from the green-cell output yields a signal proportional only to log (α). The value of either R_1 or R_2 must be adjusted so that the constant of proportionality will be the same in each case.

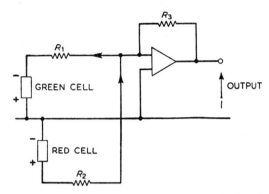

FIG. 7.19. Ratio by subtraction of logarithmic signals.

ULTRASONICS

A distinction is drawn between ultrasonics, which refers to sound *frequencies* above the audible range, and supersonics which refers to *velocities* greater than that of sound in a medium. Ultrasonics is becoming increasingly important for the location of flaws in castings, aircraft structures, components, etc. It is also a serious competitor to light beams and photoelectric devices for counting objects, detecting intruders, etc. Brief descriptions of the two main sensing principles used in ultrasonics, namely piezoelectricity and magnetostriction, are given in Chapters 2 and 6 respectively.

Ultrasonic generators and sensing devices must be correctly matched to the working medium. When two media are in contact a plane ultrasonic wave will pass through at right angles to the interface without attenuation if the characteristic impedances R of the two media are equal. The characteristic impedance is the product of the longitudinal wave velocity c and the density ρ. So long as the two values of ρc at an interface are of the same order of magnitude, serious loss does not occur. More precisely, it can be shown that the transmission and reflection coefficients α_t and α_r, giving the proportions of energy transmitted and reflected respectively, are given by

$$\alpha_t = 4R_1R_2/(R_1+R_2)^2 \quad \text{and} \quad \alpha_r = (R_2-R_1)^2/(R_1+R_2)^2.$$

When an acoustic wave travels through any medium, solid, liquid or gaseous, it experiences an attenuation which is usually observed as heat. A measure of the attenuation is the absorption coefficient of the material. A calorimetric

10

sensing device illustrating these properties is shown in Fig. 7.20. The characteristic impedances match fairly well whereas the absorption coefficient of castor oil is 1000 times that of water. Hence the castor oil absorbs acoustic energy, becoming warm in the process.

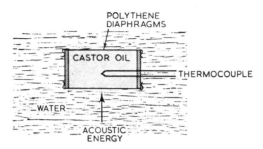

FIG. 7.20. Acoustic calorimeter.

Ultrasonic Flaw-detection

There are a number of modes of oscillation and arrangements that may be employed to examine objects for flaws. Two of these are given here as examples. Fig. 7.21 shows the direct-echo method, perhaps the simplest of all. The same transducer may serve both for transmitting and receiving;

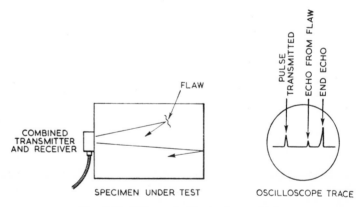

FIG. 7.21. Ultrasonic direct-echo method.

alternatively separate transducers may be used. A reflection obtained from any flaw in the material is quite distinct from a reflection from the end wall. Usually a layer of oil or other liquid is used to couple the transducer to the work piece. A method of increasing importance uses surface waves (Rayleigh waves); Fig. 7.22 shows a transducer designed for this mode of operation by the Ultrasonoscope Company (London) Ltd. Plane waves from a barium-titanate disc are split up at the Perspex/metal interface. Some of the energy continues as Rayleigh waves and some is reflected and absorbed by multi-reflections within the slipper-shaped transducer. This method is very sensitive to fine surface cracks and has proved invaluable for detecting the imminence of fatigue fracture in aircraft components.

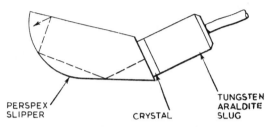

PERSPEX SLIPPER   CRYSTAL   TUNGSTEN ARALDITE SLUG

FIG. 7.22. Surface wave transducer. (*Ultrasonoscope Co. (London) Ltd.*)

Ultrasonic Object-detection

Two different methods in common use are illustrated in Figs. 7.23(*a*) and (*b*). In (*a*) the transmitter is continuously energized and a signal is obtained from the sensor whenever there is a clear path between. In (*b*) the transmitter

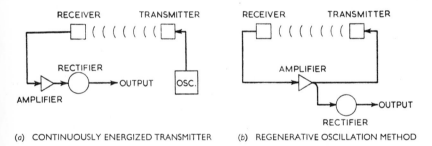

(*a*) CONTINUOUSLY ENERGIZED TRANSMITTER   (*b*) REGENERATIVE OSCILLATION METHOD

FIG. 7.23. Two methods of ultrasonic object detection.

and receiver are connected to the output and input of an amplifier, and set up a regenerative oscillation in the 'clear-path' condition. A commercial equipment which works on this principle is the 'Sonac' system. A number of the accessories available for the Sonac equipment are shown in Fig. 7.24. The equipment may be used on a direct beam between transmitter and receiver in which case the separation can be up to 30 ft. It is possible to obtain a reflection from objects that require to be sensed, in which case the transmitter and receiver are mounted close together and directed towards the expected object. As the operation is unaffected by dirt and moisture it offers advantages over systems where these hazards are prevalent. An ultrasonic level-measuring method and a viscometer using an ultrasonic technique are described elsewhere in this chapter.

The full potentialities of ultrasonic science have almost certainly not yet been realized. Some idea of what is possible is given by the ability of bats to fly through whirling fan blades and avoid criss-crossed wires by their own ultrasonic radar. They even seem to be able to recognize the terrain over which they are flying and return to their homes after quite long flights entirely by means of ultrasonic echoes.

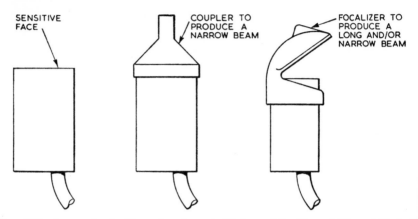

Fig. 7.24. Accessories for 'Sonac' equipment. (*Delavan Mfg. Co. and Westool Limited*)

RADIOACTIVE SENSORS

This section is concerned with sensors of radiation and particles, and with the use of radioactive methods for sensing other quantities. Descriptions of the most important radiation-sensing principles and devices are given in their respective chapters. Semiconductor barrier-layer sensors and the neutron thermopile are described in Chapter 2, while the ionization chamber, proportional counter and Geiger counter are described in Chapter 4.

Very sensitive detectors can be made using photomultipliers (see Chapter 4) in which light energy is used as an intermediate. Certain materials emit light (or 'scintillate') under the action of incident particles and the emitted light is optically coupled to the cathode of a photomultiplier. The scintillating material may be in gaseous, liquid, or solid form and a wide variety is commercially available. A mechanism similar in effect to normal scintillation is Cerenkov radiation: this is the blue glow emitted when particles pass through a material in which the particle velocity is greater than the velocity of light in the medium. Cerenkov detectors are coupled to photomultipliers in the same way as scintillators.

Fig. 7.25 shows a sectional view of a very sensitive scintillation head unit manufactured by Nuclear Enterprises (G.B.) Ltd., incorporating a heavy lead shielding to keep out as much external radiation as possible. The head is suitable for measuring the very weak radiation from small samples placed in the sample cell. Scintillation is obtained either from the material of the sample cell or from a scintillating liquid in which the sample is dissolved. A

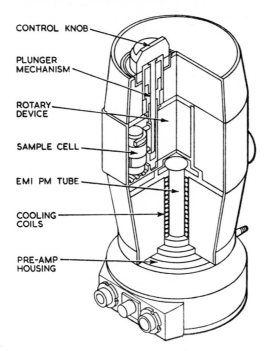

CONTROL KNOB

PLUNGER
MECHANISM

ROTARY
DEVICE

SAMPLE CELL

EMI PM TUBE

COOLING
COILS

PRE-AMP
HOUSING

FIG. 7.25. Sensitive scintillation head unit. (*Nuclear Enterprises (G.B.) Ltd.*)

feature of this model is a rotary loading device which acts as a light trap, keeping the photomultiplier in darkness during changes of sample. This makes use of the fact that after a long period in total darkness the 'dark' current of a photomultiplier decreases to a very low value. A silicone oil film between the sample cell and photomultiplier screen acts as an efficient light coupler. Cold-water cooling coils are incorporated to maintain the photomultiplier at constant temperature. Another version of this head incorporates a flow cell for the continuous monitoring of liquids or gases.

Detectors using Radioactive Techniques

Mention has already been made of gas chromatography detectors and a vacuum measuring device in Chapter 4. Other examples are level detectors and thickness measuring methods, quoted earlier in this chapter.

FOREIGN-BODY DETECTION

A most important problem in a number of industries manufacturing consumer goods is the detection and elimination of particles of foreign matter that inadvertently find their way into the products. The general public has now become trained to expect a high standard of purity and regards it almost as a point of honour to report foreign particles even if they are, in fact, harmless. Another important requirement for foreign-body detection arises with grinding or crushing equipment in mining operations for metal ores. The hazard here is of picks, shovels and other tools being lost and conveyed with the ore into the mill with consequent damage to the mill and loss of the tools.

The two principal ways of examining the inside of objects from the outside are radiography and electromagnetic induction. Radiography displays the presence and position of objects by their differing X-ray absorption from the medium in which they are situated; metal detectors are only able to indicate the presence of pieces of metal in an otherwise metal-free object.

X-rays differ in their penetrating power. Very penetrative X-rays, termed *hard* X-rays, are generated from high-voltage sources. In contrast, *soft* X-rays are derived from comparatively low-voltage sources and have low penetrating power. The target material in the X-ray tube also has an important bearing on hardness or softness. When examining objects for foreign particles it is necessary to use a suitable X-ray beam. It would be of no use attempting to detect fish bones in a packet of frozen fish using hard X-rays because they are so highly penetrating that there would be very little difference in absorption. An acceptable image would be obtained, however, using soft X-rays. Although it is possible to detect most foreign bodies by radiography, the problems of applying it to industrial production lines have not all been solved; one is that of interpreting the image. Constant peering at an X-ray picture as mass produced articles pass by is at best tedious, and operators are not likely to be very effective for more than short periods at a time.

It would be a good approach to scan the X-ray beam over the product with a detector behind it and interpret electronically the waveform so obtained. Unfortunately it is not easy to scan an X-ray beam and no means of doing it on a convenient scale have yet been found. Another approach is to produce a radiographic picture, look at this picture with a television camera and then evaluate the image electronically for foreign bodies. This is expensive, but it may well prove to be the only solution for a long while to come.

Although metal-detectors do not detect glass, wood, plastic and other injurious foreign bodies they are used widely for finding metal objects. Their operating principles are discussed in Chapter 6. The sensitivity (or smallness of body that can be found) depends on the aperture size. With apertures suitable for small packets of food products foreign bodies of the order of

1–2 mm diameter can be detected. Smaller apertures, for example for packets of pharmaceutical tablets, can detect even smaller objects. In quarrying applications where very large apertures are required the detection of small objects is neither desirable, necessary nor possible. Sometimes even non-metallic articles can be specially tagged so that they can be found again. Industrial surgical dressings can be obtained incorporating a foil strip so that their presence in any product will be detected. Surgical swabs can also be similarly 'labelled' so that a patient can be examined during an operation with a metal-detector to ensure that no swabs are left inside before closing up an incision. More bizarre applications sometimes arise, such as metal-detectors fixed around doorways to detect the presence of concealed arms or stolen goods.

Having detected the foreign body, it must be removed. The simplest procedure is to make the detector stop the conveyor belt and ring a bell so that the particle can be removed manually. Automatic means suitable for packets can be obtained, whereby an offending packet is automatically removed from the production line for later examination. In a modification, used when a layer of powder or granular materials on a conveyer belt is examined, a portion of the material is diverted to a holding bin for later examination. Since it is never convenient to divert a packet at the instant the foreign body is found, some form of delay is required so that ejection takes place at a later point in the travel. Sometimes when the material is subject to a subsequent manual inspection the presence of a foreign body is indicated with a squirt of dye or powder, or by the release of a marker tag.

Metal-detection can also be used on liquids, but foreign bodies can usually be eliminated from liquids more conveniently by filtration.

VISCOSITY

Viscosity is very much a mechanical quantity and most of the methods of measuring it operate by entirely mechanical means. There are, however, two types of instrument that employ electronic methods. In one a cup or disc is rotated at constant speed in the liquid and the torque required to do so is measured. The size of the cup or disc is determined by the range of viscosities being measured. The resulting torque can be measured mechanically or by means of an electrical transducer.

The Bendix Ultra-Viscoson is a viscometer that operates by the damping effect of a liquid on a reed vibrating at an ultrasonic frequency. The reed is made of steel, is about 6 in. long, and has a natural frequency of about 23 kc/s. A coil wound round one end of the blade induces vibrations by magnetostriction. Viscosity is measured by pulsing the coil which sets the reed vibrating. The damping effect of the liquid attenuates the vibrations, which are monitored by the coil. When the vibrations have decreased to a predetermined level another current pulse is applied. Thus the repetition frequency of current pulses varies with the viscosity. An electronic unit provides the pulses and conditions the output signal to give a reading in terms of viscosity.

REFERENCES

Blitz, J. *Fundamentals of Ultrasonics*, Butterworths, London (1963).

Carroll, G. C. (ed.), *Industrial Process Measuring Instruments*, McGraw-Hill Book Company, Inc., New York (1962).

Cook, N. H. and Rabinowicz, E. *Physical Measurement and Analysis*, Addison-Wesley Publishing Co. Inc., Reading, Mass. (1963).

Grabbe, E. M., Ramo, S. and Wooldridge, D. E. (eds.), *Handbook of Automation, Computation & Control, Volume 3, Systems and Components*, John Wiley & Sons, Inc., New York (1961).

Lytel, A. *Industrial Electronics*, McGraw-Hill Book Company, Inc., New York (1962).

Minnar, E. J. (ed.), *I.S.A. Transducer Compendium*, Plenum Press, New York (1963).

CHAPTER 8

ELECTRONIC SENSORS FOR CHEMISTRY

The purpose of this chapter is to review some of the sensing devices and methods of importance in chemistry. In most cases only references will be given as descriptions appear elsewhere in the book under the headings of the various electronic phenomena. In its discussion of electrolytic sensing devices, Chapter 3 deals with the measurement of pH and with electro-chemical analysis techniques such as polarography. Another powerful analytical method, mass spectrometry, is discussed in Chapter 4. In these two subjects electronics is not merely a convenient tool but is a link with the fundamental electrical nature of matter.

The chapter is divided into two parts, the first dealing with the detection of specific substances and the second with electronic devices as an aid to particular methods of chemical analysis.

DETECTION OF SPECIFIC SUBSTANCES

Moisture Measurement

The measurement of the water content of solids, liquids and gases has received considerable attention during the last few decades, but it has in many cases defied an ideal solution. Indeed, most of the phenomena in this book have at some time or other been investigated to find if they could be used for measuring water content. The humidity of air is vital to our existence, yet is not appreciated so well as other phenomena of far less importance. This is because the human body is unable to *sense* humidity directly; it can only register discomfort in excessive heat and humidity. Most humidity sensors (such as wet- and dry-bulb thermometers) are very slow in response and give the impression that humidity is a rather uninteresting physical property of air. With the rapidly-responding electronic humidity sensors now available, however, a very different picture of humidity is built up. The swirling clouds of water vapour given off by human beings are detectable and show that, in all but the most static situations, air and water vapour make anything but a homogeneous mixture. A rapid sensor for demonstrating this effect uses a special capacitor with aluminium oxide as dielectric. The method suffers greatly from temperature-dependence, which is difficult or impossible to compensate, so will probably not be applied to humidity measurement in general.

Among the standard methods of measuring humidity the conductivity hygrometers mentioned in Chapter 3 are perhaps the simplest. A more sophisticated method uses a lithium-chloride element (which is highly hygroscopic) together with a pair of electrodes. As water vapour is absorbed it is electrolysed, raising the temperature of the lithium chloride. An equilibrium temperature is soon reached where water vapour is electrolysed as fast as it is absorbed. This 'dewpoint' temperature is then measured by a thermocouple or resistance thermometer from which a value of relative humidity can be derived.

A thermocouple or resistance thermometer version of the conventional wet- and dry-bulb method is often very convenient, especially when a multipoint temperature recorder is being used, as a wet bulb can easily be added as a separate point on the recorder. Special psychrometers are manufactured in which air is blown at a constant rate over the wet bulb. The rate of air flow is, however, not critical and can often be successfully provided by an electric fan. When making up wet-bulb thermocouples from stock materials such as iron, copper, constantan, etc., it is important to protect the metals from water by a layer of varnish or other suitable material to prevent corrosion which would otherwise rapidly set in. Another traditional method has been given a new look in the Peltier-effect dewpoint apparatus. This uses a semiconductor thermoelectric cold junction to cool a metal mirror until a layer of dew forms. A beam of light reflected from the mirror on to a photocell is dispersed when the dew forms and a signal from the photocell reduces the thermopile current. The temperature then either oscillates slightly about the dew point or stabilizes with a thin dew film. The temperature of the metal mirror is thus the dewpoint of the atmosphere.

Humidity instruments may be calibrated either by vaporizing a known quantity of water in a chamber of known volume, or by use of constant-humidity bottles. These are based on the equilibrium between saturated salt solutions and the vapour above them. Table 8.1 gives some typical salts used together with their equilibrium humidities.

The water-vapour content of process-gas streams can often be measured at high precision with the electrolysis analyser mentioned in Chapter 3. Other methods make use of the absorption of infra-red radiation or the attenuation of an ultrasonic beam.

The measurement of a small proportion of water dissolved in other liquids can often be made by virtue of its higher relative permittivity. The liquid is made to flow through a sample cell, usually of concentric construction, where the permittivity can be measured. The hardest problems c

Table 8.1. Data for Constant Humidity Bottles. (Correct at 20°C)*

Substance	Humidity per cent
Lead nitrate $Pb(NO_3)_2$	98
Zinc sulphate $ZnSO_4.7H_2O$	90
Ammonium sulphate $(NH_4)_2SO_4$	81
Ammonium chloride NH_4Cl and potassium nitrate KNO_3	72·6
Sodium bromide $NaBr.2H_2O$	58
Potassium thiocyanate $KCNS$	47
Zinc nitrate $Zn(NO_3)_2.6H_2O$	42
Calcium chloride $CaCl_2.6H_2O$	32·3
Potassium acetate CH_3COOK	20
Lithium chloride $LiCl.H_2O$	15

* Data selected from *Handbook of Chemistry and Physics*, 44th. ed. Chemical Rubber Publishing Company, Cleveland, Ohio.

evaluation of water content occur with solid materials. Water may be present, either free or bound, to a greater or lesser extent. The free and bound components usually respond differently to measurements of conductivity, permittivity, etc. If the relative proportions of free and bound moisture are not known and are variable, the measurement can be very difficult. Yet some successes must be recorded; the grain-moisture analyser described in Chapter 5 is such a case. Another method which has proved successful in many applications involves a measurement of the attenuation of a microwave beam.

There are commercial equipments available for measuring the moisture content of all sorts of materials in common use. These measure either conductivity or permittivity, and no doubt operate satisfactorily in limited situations where there are no great variations of the material characteristics.

Oxygen Analysers

Oxygen is vital to most forms of life. Oxygen analysers are used to check that the concentration is high enough to preserve life in space vehicles, submarines, industrial plant, rivers, lakes, etc. Another kind of application uses oxygen analysers to check that the oxygen concentration is low enough in particular situations, as in boiler feedwater, in boiler flue gases or in gas-packed foodstuffs. A simple dissolved-oxygen analyser suitable for the boiler feedwater application, described in Chapter 3, operates by generating a galvanic potential. A more widely applicable oxygen probe using a polarographic technique is also described.

Oxygen is paramagnetic, and a family of oxygen analysers depends on this property. One type of instrument uses a ferrous-metal object suspended in a non-linear magnetic field. When oxygen is present the field round the object is disturbed and a different balance position is obtained. The deflection from the original position is thus a measure of oxygen content. Another instrument is illustrated diagrammatically in Fig. 8.1. This makes use of the loss of paramagnetism of a material when heated above its Curie temperature. The gas containing oxygen is drawn by the attraction of its oxygen content into the magnetic field. When in the field it is heated by a resistance-heater wire

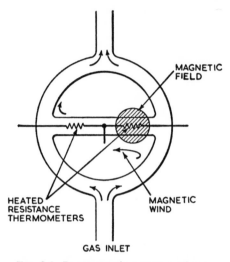

FIG. 8.1. Paramagnetic oxygen analyser.

above the Curie temperature, causing it to become non-magnetic. It is then pushed out by more cold gas and a 'magnetic wind' is created. A second resistance-heater wire is also fixed to the centre tube and the gas-flow through the tube is measured by the difference in temperature of the two resistance wires. This part of the instrument is similar to the thermal flowmeter described in Chapter 2.

Catalytic Gas-detector

When a combustible gas mixed with air comes in contact with a suitable catalyst, combustion takes place on the surface of the catalyst, raising its temperature. Under suitable conditions the catalyst can become hot enough to ignite the gas, a principle used in certain types of gas lighters. The same principle is the basis of a number of combustible-gas detectors described here. The catalyst may be a platinum wire, finely divided platinum, or mixtures including other rare metals such as palladium. While some gases react at ambient temperatures, others only do so if the catalyst is pre-heated and this together with variation of types of catalyst used enables some degree of specificity to be obtained. The catalyst does not itself become exhausted but it may be poisoned if certain gases are present. It is also possible to construct detectors in which the gas reacts with a solid material, raising its temperature. In this case it is necessary to renew the solid reagent from time to time.

Fig. 8.2 shows three variants of the catalytic method. The arrangement (*a*) can be used if a representative gas sample can be obtained for reference. This

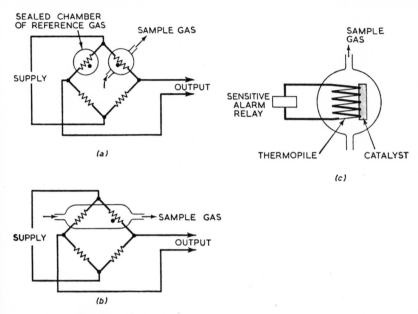

FIG. 8.2. Three arrangements for catalytic gas detection.

would not be admissible if the gas composition changes appreciably, and particularly if the filaments are initially heated, as different gases may cause a spurious imbalance due to their unequal thermal conductivities—the basis of katharometry. The filaments are usually platinum wire either plain or wound round a support containing catalytic material. The arrangement (*b*) over-comes the problem of varying gas composition as both filaments are in con-tact with the sample gas. An output is obtained because only one of the two filaments is activated with catalyst. The third arrangement (*c*) is able to operate a sensitive relay directly, but no pre-heating is possible.

Detectors based on these principles play an important part in mining and industrial undertakings both for protecting personnel against gases such as carbon monoxide, and for monitoring explosion hazards. In order to prevent the catalyst from igniting the main body of gas if it becomes red hot, a metal gauze screen (like the screen on a Davy lamp) is used to isolate it. Another important application is for detecting leaks of ammonia gas from refrigera-tion compressor plant.

ELECTRONIC AIDS TO ANALYTICAL METHODS

Gas Chromatography

The number of specific detectors that respond to only one material is severely limited. Even those used for detecting water, oxygen or ammonia are only specific when certain materials are excluded or known not to be present. Gas chromatography is a method of taking a mixture of compounds, separating them and parading each compound in turn before a detector. The main part of a chromatograph is the column, which may be straight or spiral, filled with an adsorbent material. A controlled flow of a carrier gas is passed through the column and through a detector at the far end. The mixture to be analysed is injected in a short burst into the carrier gas just before it enters the column. The various components of the mixture transit the column at different speeds, and so a kind of separated spectrum appears at the end, to be sensed by the detector. It is, of course, important that the detector response of the separated compounds should differ from that of the carrier gas.

Descriptions of detectors for gas chromatography appear elsewhere. The katharometer is described in Chapter 2, while the cross-section, argon, electron-capture and flame-ionization detectors are described in Chapter 4.

The transit time of the column is affected greatly by temperature changes, making precise temperature control necessary. For some mixtures the transit time at a particular temperature of some compounds is very short, while for others it is inconveniently long. A rough 'logarithmic' compression to accommodate all the compounds in a reasonable time is obtained by programming the column temperature. This is done by starting at a certain temperature and raising the temperature at a controlled and steady rate. The fast-transit compounds go through the cold column at a convenient speed and as the column warms up the more sluggish compounds are helped on their way.

Infra-red Gas-analysers

When a beam of infra-red energy is passed through a gas, certain portions of the spectrum are absorbed, different parts by different gases. A number of instruments commercially available for analysing gases use this principle. A schematic diagram of one, the Analytic System Company's series 700, is shown in Fig. 8.3. There are two paths through the apparatus and infra-red energy from hot wire filaments is sent down both paths. The energy is chopped into simultaneous pulses at 20 c/s by a rotating shutter. The reference gas in filter cell A is chosen to have absorption bands separate from those of the gases to be analysed. The detector is made specific to a particular gas by putting a sample of the gas in filter cell B. When any other gas is introduced into the sample chambers equal attenuation occurs and no output is obtained. When the selected gas is present in the sample chambers no absorption by the gas takes place in sample cell B as all the energy has been removed from the specific bands by the filter gas. A normal amount of absorption occurs in channel A so an unbalance is caused which can be sensed by the detectors.

The detectors are chambers filled with gases which expand under the heating effect of the absorbed infra-red energy. The expansion is detected by an arrangement basically identical to a capacitor microphone. The detector cells are connected by a small-bore pipe so that long-term unbalances in the system do not cause an output. A feature of the Analytic System Company's equipment is the self-balancing amplifier, in which the polarizing voltage of the channel A microphone is adjusted by a feedback loop to give zero a.c. difference output between the microphones. This arrangement is conducive to high stability.

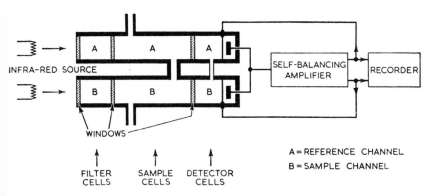

FIG. 8.3. Infra-red gas analyser. (*Analytic Systems Company*)

Future Techniques

There are many other techniques of increasing importance in which electronics plays an indispensable role a description of which is outside the scope of this book. Electron paramagnetic resonance, nuclear magnetic resonance, microwave absorption, spectroscopy, polarimetry, refractometry, etc., are all techniques capable of further development for the sensing of physical effects.

REFERENCES

Ambrose, D. and Ambrose, B. A. *Gas Chromatography*, George Newnes, Ltd., London (1961).
Littlewood, A. B. *Gas Chromatography*, Academic Press, London (1962).
Parr, N. L. (ed.). *Laboratory Handbook*, George Newnes Ltd., London, (1963).
Stalhuth, W. E. 'Moisture Measurement and Control', *Automation* (Nov. 1963).

(See also references to Chapter 3.)

REFERENCES TO MANUFACTURERS

Airmec Ltd.,
  High Wycombe, Bucks.
Analytic Systems Company,
  370 South Fair Oaks Avenue, Pasadena, Calif.
ASEA (G.B.) Ltd.,
  41, Strand, London, W.C.2.
Atlas Mess- und Analysentechnik GmbH,
  Bremen, West Germany,
  U.K. Agents: Europa Engineering Co. Ltd., 12A, Golden Square, London, W.1.
Beckman Instruments, Inc.,
  Fullerton, California; Glenrothes, Fife, Scotland.
Bendix Corporation, Cincinnati Div.,
  3625 Hauck Rd., Cincinnati 41, Ohio.
Brion Leroux,
  40, Quai de Jemmapes, Paris 10,
  U.K. Agents: Leland Instruments Ltd., 145, Grosvenor Road, Westminster, London, S.W.1.
British Aircraft Corporation,
  Electrolevel marketed by: G. V. Planer Ltd., Windmill Road, Sunbury-on-Thames, Middx.
Consolidated Electrodynamics Corporation,
  Transducer Division, 1400 South Shamrock Avenue, Monrovia, Calif.
  Bell & Howell Ltd., Consolidated Electrodynamics Div., 14, Commercial Road, Woking, Surrey.
Coulter Electronics Industrial Division,
  2525 N. Sheffield Ave, Chicago, Ill.
  Coulter Electronics Ltd., 2–4, Ashwell St., St. Albans, Herts.
Decker Corporation, The,
  Bala-Cynwyd, Pennsylvania.
Delavan Mfg. Co.
  Iowa.
Dracone Developments Ltd.,
  P.O. Box 18, Calshot Spit, Fawley, Hants.
Electronic Switchgear (London) Ltd.,
  Wilbury Way, Hitchin, Herts.

Endress & Hauser GmbH,
   7867 Maulburg, Postfach 20, Germany.
   U.K. Agents: Dukes & Briggs Engineering Co. Ltd., Approach Road
   (Barton Dock Road), Urmston, Manchester.

Fielden Electronics Ltd.,
   Wythenshawe, Manchester.

G.E.C. (Engineering) Ltd.,
   Birmingham 6, England.

Gloster Equipment Ltd.,
   Gloucester, England.

Hamlin Inc.,
   Lake Mills, Wisconsin.
   U.K. Agents: Flight Refuelling, Industrial Electronics Div., Wimborne, Dorset.

Hays Corporation, The,
   Michigan City, Indiana.

Industrial Instruments, Inc.,
   89 Commerce Road, Cedar Grove, Essex County, N.J.
   U.K. Agents: D. A. Pitman Ltd., 91, Heath Road, Weybridge, Surrey.

Lippke, Paul,
   Neuwied/Rhein, West Germany.
   U.K. Agents: Orthos (Engineering) Ltd., 62, Coventry Road, Market
   Harborough, Leics.

Loenco, Inc.,
   2092 N. Lincoln Ave., Altadena, Calif.
   U.K. Agents: D. A. Pitman Ltd., 91, Heath Road, Weybridge, Surrey.

Mawdsley's Ltd.,
   Dursley, Gloucestershire.

Micrometrical Division, The Bendix Corporation,
   3621 South State Road, Ann Arbor, Michigan.
   U.K. Agents: Gaston E. Marbaix, Ltd., Devonshire House, Vicarage
   Crescent, London, S.W.11.

Mine Safety Appliances Company,
   201 N. Braddock Avenue, Pittsburgh 8, Pa.
   Queenslie Industrial Estate, Glasgow, E.3.

Mullard Ltd.,
   Mullard House, Torrington Place, London, W.C.1.

Nuclear Enterprises (G.B.) Ltd.,
   Sighthill, Edinburgh, Scotland.

Perkin-Elmer Corporation,
   Norwalk, Connecticut.

Philips', N.V. Gloeilampenfabrieken,
   Eindhoven, Netherlands.

Photocon Research Products,
   421 N. Altadena Drive, Pasadena, Calif.

RCA
   Electron Tube Plant, Lancaster, Pennsylvania.
   RCA (G.B.) Ltd., Lincoln Way, Windmill Road,
   Sunbury-on-Thames, Middx.

chaevitz Engineering,
   P.O. Box 505, Camden 1, New Jersey.
   U.K. Agents: Electro Mechanisms Ltd., 220, Bedford Ave., Slough, Bucks.
elf-Organising Systems, Inc.,
   P.O. Box 9918, Dallas, Texas.
iemens & Halske Aktiengesellschaft,
   Karlsruhe, West Germany.
   Siemens (United Kingdom) Ltd., Great West House, Great West Road,
   Brentford, Middx.
miths Industries Ltd., Industrial Div.
   New North Road, Hainault, Ilford, Essex.
ogenique (Electronics) Ltd.,
ociete Genevoise Ltd.,
   Newport Pagnell, Bucks.
ann Controls Company,
   3750 E. Outer Drive, Detroit 34, Michigan.
   U.K. Agents: Airmec Ltd., High Wycombe, Bucks.
eledictor Ltd.,
   Groveland Road, Tipton, Staffs.
elomex Ltd.,
   Queen Street, Horsham, Sussex.
)th Century Electronics Ltd.,
   Centronic Works, King Henry's Drive, New Addington, Croydon, Surrey.
ltrasonoscope Co. (London) Ltd.,
   Sudbourne Road, London, S.W.2.
ayne Kerr Laboratories Ltd.,
   44, Coombe Road, New Malden, Surrey.
   Wayne Kerr Corporation, 1633 Race Street, Philadelphia 3, Pa.
estool Ltd.,
   St. Helen's Auckland, Bishop Auckland, Co. Durham.

INDEX

155